The Sun Rose Late

by

JOHN FRASCA

and

MICHAEL HARRIS

ISBN 87637 - 168 - 3

Library of Congress Catalog No. 74 - 83698

Dedicated To The Memory of
Major Clark Stone
U.S. Army

CHAPTER ONE

Charley Woods was 23 and just the right age for those who believe they are invincible. You had to believe you were unbeatable to fly the Hump day after day, snaking through the treacherous tops of the snow crusted Himalayas with a four-engine plane loaded with 28,000 pounds of aviation gasoline. It didn't shake Charley's faith in his own survivability when some of his buddies vanished in the mysterious valleys of the mountains that guarded the entrance to the Plateau of Tibet and the plains of China beyond. He never doubted that some day he would return to his home in Alabama and the wife and baby son who were waiting for him to end the war, not even when others of his friends were consumed by the exploding flames that almost always came when one of the flying tank cars crashed on take-off or landing.

Some B-24 Liberators had been converted from bombers to fuel carriers. The huge gas containers in the belly invited the ripping thrust of a stump on a ragged field, to summon the igniting attention of a vagrant spark. These fuel carriers were designated as C-109's. Charley called them "See One Oh Boom," never thinking that any plane he flew would go boom. He never considered for a moment that he wouldn't make it, although he already had flirted with the law of averages for three years, flying practically everything there was to fly since he joined the Royal Canadian Air Force in March of 1941, when he, at 19, was one of the few Americans to recognize that Hitler was more than a funny little man with a moustache. With casualties mounting on every front, Charley rejected the thought that he, too, might become a statistic.

It was warm for December, even in Kurmitola, India. Charley, still in his flight suit, slept on top of his cot in the tent he shared with his buddy, Ralph Keele. He had returned at 9:00 that morning, December 23, 1944, after another round-trip over the Hump from Kurmitola to Lulaing, China. He had delivered a load of fuel to the Flying Tigers, who were fighting a separate war with the Japanese based in Manchuria, and had slept for an hour under the wing while ground crews emptied the tanks. On his return, expecting to be assigned to another flight, he had fallen onto his cot with his clothes still on. This way, he could steal a few minutes more sleep. It was 11:00 when he hit the sack, after filling out his report in the operations shack, breakfasting with his crew in the Mess Hall and reading the latest letter from Miriam. She wrote every day, but the letters were always three or four weeks late in coming. He tried to write her at least once a week, either from Kurmitola or one of the Allied bases in China.

Charley woke to the firm grip of a hand shaking his shoulder. He looked up at Marty Hendricks, the operations clerk.

"Hey, Marty," he said. "I guess I'm going again. Right?"

"That's right, sir. You're scheduled to fly check this time for a new pilot, Captain Stalmacher."

"Stalmacher? I don't think I've met him, Marty."

"He's flown a few trips as co-pilot, captain. This is his first shot at being an aircraft commander. You're supposed to break him in."

"Well, as long as he's been over the Hump before. He knows what it is to fight those winds up there. Where we going, Marty?"

"Back to Lulaing, sir. You'd better hustle, captain. Time of departure is 1730. You've got a little more than an hour to get briefed and all."

Charley looked at his wristwatch. It said 4 o'clock.

"Okay, Marty. I'll be right along. What did you say this pilot's name was?"

"Stalmacher, sir."

Charley walked to the operations shack to check the weather and study the flight plan, which was more habit than necessity. He had flown to and from Lulaing at least 100 times already. The weather in the Himalayas was always bad. If it wasn't snowing, it was sleeting. There was always the danger of ice accumulating on the wings and frosting the windshield. Long ago, he had learned the trick of losing the ice by dropping into the warmer air between the lower peaks.

He met Stalmacher and Donald Hoag, the flight engineer at the operations shack. Hoag introduced the two captains.

"How many times you been over the Hump?" asked Charley.

"I've flown co-pilot six or seven times already," said Stalmacher. "This is my first trip as first pilot."

"Well, you know how this baby handles," said Charley.

"That's right," said Stalmacher. "The C.O. thinks I'm ready for my own plane."

5

"What matters is do you think you're ready?" said Charley.

"Heck, captain, I've been ready a long time."

The jeep took the trio to the field. Charley and Stalmacher discussed the flight while ground personnel prepared the big plane for the 500-mile trip. Hoag was joined by the radio operator, Skip Rodriguez.

"She's ready, sir," said the ground chief.

"Okay," said Charley. "Let's go, boys."

Hoag and Rodriguez climbed through the bomb bay. Charley followed, and then Stalmacher. The two enlisted men took their places in the rear of the plane. Charley and Stalmacher crawled into their seats.

"Don't worry about me, captain," said Stalmacher, smiling. "I can handle her all right."

"I figured you could," said Charley, responding with a grin, giving warmth for warmth. "I guess you know she's carrying 28,000 pounds of gas and she weighs sixty-five thousand pounds. She needs plenty of runway to take off. She's tough to handle on the ground. It'll take 120 miles an hour to get her off the runway."

"Yes, yes, I know, captain," Stalmacher replied. "Are we ready to start rolling?"

"Ready," Charley said.

Stalmacher held the propeller pitch levers forward, all mixture knobs full rich, and worked the throttle. Charlie pressed the starter for each engine. Numbers 3, 1, 2 and 4 fired to life. All needles on the instrument panel slipped into the green. Charley radioed Kurmitola Tower for taxi instructions.

"You are cleared to taxi," the tower operator said. "Runway three-six. Wind north northeast. Five knots.

Altimeter setting two-nine nine-five. Four-five past the hour. Over."

Charley nodded to Stalmacher who released the brakes and prepared to taxi. Charley advised the tower they were preparing to proceed to the runway.

Stalmacher cautiously inched the four throttles forward, too cautiously, thought Charley. The B-24 didn't move. Charley looked at Stalmacher. He pushed the throttles forward a little more. The plane began to move, slowly. The four big engines, each spinning three-bladed propellers, roared louder and louder. The vibration shook Charley and Stalmacher. The plane picked up speed. Charley could visualize what the ground crews were seeing as the big Liberator pushed forward, huge black wheels squashed almost flat by the tons of machine and gasoline.

Charley watched Stalmacher's face as the first pilot eased the plane onto the runup area. He was being too deliberate, thought Charley, as though he were following a routine he had rehearsed in his mind. You're supposed to do this. You're supposed to do that. There, I did that right. Good. Now, let me do this right. Stalmacher wasn't loose enough. He was too tight, too determined.

As commander of the plane, Charley wondered what would happen if he radioed the tower and said they were coming back in. What was he going to say? That he didn't think Stalmacher should be flying? What made him think so? Well, he was being too careful, you know. He wanted to make sure he was doing everything exactly right. Was that all? Is there something wrong, captain, with being careful and doing everything exactly right?

It was just a fleeting thought. Charley knew that Stalmacher had been sent there to fly, and that's what he'd do. With a little practice, he might turn out to be the best of the lot of them. He'd just watch him, that's all, and if he did anything wrong he'd take over immediately.

Stalmacher moved the plane to the head of the runway. Charley called off the items on the two-page check list. "Check," said Stalmacher. "Check." Everything checked. Charley called Hoag and Rodriguez on the intercom. They were ready. He radioed Kurmitola Tower.

"B-24 ready for take-off," he said.

"You are cleared for immediate take off," said the tower. "Have a good flight."

"Dear God, please be with us," whispered Charley, and he gave the go-ahead nod to Stalmacher.

Stalmacher pushed the throttles to the firewall and held the brakes while the engines reached full power. He held the plane in position for a few seconds while Charley checked the instruments again. He released the brakes. The Liberator began to move. There was no surge of speed. The converted tanker was too heavy for that. But, as the twelve spinning blades bit into the night air, she began to pick up speed, roaring down the 6,000-foot ribbon of lighted asphalt. Charley called out the numbers after she reached 80 miles an hour.

"Ninety," he said. "Ninety-five. One hundred."

At 100, Stalmacher lifted the nose.

"She's too high," called out Charley. "Lower your nose."

Stalmacher lowered the nose.

"One hundred ten," said Charley. "One hundred fifteen. One hundred twenty."

As Charley yelled 120, Stalmacher pushed both feet against the brakes. The nose wheel pitched forward suddenly.

Charley realized that Stalmacher had thought the plane was in the air and hit the brakes to stop the wheels from spinning. In that instant, the speed dropped down to 90 miles an hour. Charley figured there was less than 600 feet of runway. Not enough room to build up to the 120-mile take-off speed.

Now, Charley Woods took over. He could make one of three choices. He could slam down on one brake. The aircraft would spin around; the gears would break loose; the gas tanks probably would rupture and the plane would explode. He could pull back on the control wheel and gamble on pulling the craft off the ground, but when that maneuver had been attempted with a B-24, Charley knew, it had stalled and mushed back to the ground and rolled into a ball of fire. In those crashes, those which he remembered, there were no survivors.

Or he could shut off the power, stand on the brakes and try to reduce her speed so that when she rolled off the runway she would sink into the dirt just after her nose wheel and main gears would be swept away, as they inevitably would be under the weight of the skidding 32-ton machine. If she were traveling slowly enough, and if Charley managed to keep her on a straight path, the plane conceivably could come to rest without ripping a tank in the belly.

In the second that the three possibilities raced through Charley's mind, Charley chose the third as the only possible way to survive. He yanked off the power and stood on the brakes. He fought the controls as the Liberator plowed off the runway into the soft dirt at the end, losing the nose wheels and gears as Charley had expected. Charley had been too busy to see what Stalmacher was doing. He glanced at him. now, and saw that he, too, was battling the controls on his side of the cabin. The plane skidded ahead, straight ahead, making a wide furrow in the jungle whose value was just enhanced by the American plane's invasion. "If he plays his cards right, that owner can get rich," thought Charley. "He can claim we damaged his field so bad that crops will never grow." The plane slowed to 60 miles an hour, 50, 40, 35, 30, 20, 10. She was coming to a stop. Then, he felt the shudder as the plane hit the protruding remains of a fallen tree. He was remembering, when the gasoline spewed out and embraced a spark, that he had been told that the trees on this land had been chopped down two years before.

"Let's get out of here," he yelled to the crew. They were the last words he heard spoken in that cockpit, quickly followed by the explosion and the hurricane of flames that enveloped them. Charley closed his eyes and held his breath, to protect his lungs from the boiling fire. He unfastened his seat belt. As he opened his eyes, for an instant to find the buckle, he saw Stalmacher beating at the flames on the chest of his flight suit. Charley opened his mouth to tell him to get out first, and the fire that his breath sucked in was warning enough to keep it closed. With his eyes shut again, Charley reached for the plexiglass panel at his shoulder and slid it open. He stepped on his parachute, which, contrary to regulations, he never wore until he was high in the air, because a parachute is no good to you until you're at least 500 feet off the ground, and pushed his head and right arm through the small opening. He twisted his body to bring out his left arm, and lunged forward to let his weight carry him to the burning ground 10 feet below.

He saw himself falling to the ground, as though in a movie set in slow-motion time, as though he was performing a part he was required to play. He felt no pain, no panic. When he was a boy he stuck his head in an oven, a little too far, to check on a baking pie, and this heat reminded him of that.

He broke the fall with his hands. He rolled over, sprang to his feet and ran for the darkness beyond the circle of fire. He stumbled and fell. He got up and ran again. He turned to look at the plane. Only the tips of the wings were visible. The rest of the big B-24 lay disintegrating inside the towering torch. Charley sat on a small mound of dirt to wait for Stalmacher, Hoag and Rodriguez. He persuaded himself to believe that they also had escaped. They were probably looking for him on the other side of the blaze. He saw, then, that the cuffs and neck of his flight suit were still smoldering. He slapped out the fire with his hands.

Soon, he was surrounded by Indians who had come out of the small houses and shacks on the outskirts of the field. Several of them helped him pull off his flight suit. Two others removed his paratrooper boots.

His eyes swelled and closed. Now, he only sensed the presence of the crowd surrounding him.

"Does anybody speak English?" he asked.

"Yes, sir," said a voice. "I'm British."

"Could you see about getting me an ambulance" said Charley, rebuking himself for saying it. What did he need an ambulance for?

"Straight away, sir," said the Briton.

"Has anybody seen the other men in my crew?" Charley asked the spectators.

Nobody answered.

CHAPTER TWO

He lay on a stretcher in an ambulance bumping across the field to the base hospital. An orderly knelt beside him and smeared vasoline over his face, neck and hands.

"Let me tell you what happened," he said. "Let me tell you what happened."

"Take it easy, captain," said the orderly, who had seen the double bars on the charred uniform a native had thrown into the back of the ambulance, along with his boots. "Take it easy. We'll be at the hospital in a couple of minutes."

"He slammed on the brakes before she got off the ground," said Charley. "We lost speed and there wasn't time to build it back up."

Charley didn't know his words were being distorted by the globs of vasoline. They only formed bubbles of incoherence.

The ambulance stopped. The orderly and the driver pulled the stretcher from the ambulance. They carried Charley through a knot of doctors and nurses who had gathered on the steps.

"Put him on this table," said a doctor. "Here, let's get this stuff off him. Clean him up so we can see what we've got."

Charley opened his eyes when the vasoline was removed from his face. He saw a nurse and a doctor bending over him.

"What happened?" said the doctor, while he examined him.

"How about my crew?" said Charley, "Did they make it?"

"Sure. Don't worry. Everybody's fine. Take it easy. How did it happen?"

"She didn't have enough room to make it so I tried to slow her down and ease her off the runway. He hit the brakes just as we reached 120 miles an hour. If he'd waited another second, we'd have been in the air. After he put on the brakes, she slowed down and there wasn't enough time to build up the speed again."

"How do you feel? Are you having any pain?"

"No, doc. It's funny, too. I don't feel bad at all. How long do you think before I'll be able to get out of here?"

"We'll see, captain. First we're going to put some ointment on those burns and wrap them up. We're going to put something on your eyes."

"Okay, doc. Say, will you send somebody for Ralph Keele? He's my tent mate."

"I'll send somebody right away."

While the nurse and doctor were working on Charley's face, head, neck and arms, Keele entered the emergency room.

"Hey, Charley. How you doing?"

"He stuck the brakes on me, Ralph."

"I thought maybe you lost an engine," said Keele as the nurse stuck a needle in his arm.

When he woke Charley heard soft voices near his bed. One was Ralph's.

"I hate to be here when he finds out," said Ralph. "Who's going to tell him?"

"I think it's best for the doctor to tell him," said another voice, a woman's voice.

Tell him what, wondered Charley. He lay still, pretending he was still asleep. At first he didn't know where he was. When he woke it was just another morning in Kurmitola, one like all of the others, wondering if he was going to have to fly the Hump again today. He opened his eyes. He couldn't see. He started to swing himself out of bed. He couldn't move. There was a weight on his face. There were weights on his hands. Then he remembered.

"Anybody here?" he said through the hole in his mask.

"Hey, Charley, how're you feeling?"

He turned his head toward the sound of Ralph's voice.

"Hi, Ralph. What time is it?"

"It's 6 o'clock, Charley."

"Morning or night, Ralph?"

"Morning, Charley."

"You were here last night, weren't you, Ralph? You've been here all night?"

"You know I hate to sleep alone," said Ralph. "Don't worry about me. I slept good. How about you?"

"I was out like a light, Ralph. It's the most sleep I've had since I've been in India."

"Good morning, captain," said the woman's voice. "Let me tell the doctor you're awake."

"Well, I'll be going, Charley," said Ralph. "I'm scheduled for a flight to Lulaing this morning. I'll be seeing you. Take it easy now."

"See you, Ralph. Good luck."

Ralph patted him on the shoulder and he left, vanishing

from Charley's life forever. He met the doctor in the doorway.

"Take care of him, doc," he said.

"We'll do our best," said the doctor, moving to Charley's side. "How do you feel this morning, captain?"

"I'm all right. What happened to my crew, doc?"

There was no answer. Charley felt the doctor's hands on the bandages covering his face.

"They're dead, aren't they?"

"Yes," he said, departing the room, leaving the single word to echo in Charley's brain.

They didn't have a chance, he thought. Poor Hoag. Poor Rodriguez. Poor Stalmacher. He could see him now, strapped in his seat, beating at the fire eating at his flight suit. He visualized Hoag and Rodriguez opening an escape hatch and being engulfed by the flames. It was a miracle that he escaped. But had he?

The doctor returned.

"Captain," he said, "we're sending you to the Royal Victoria in Calcutta. They have the facilities to take care of you."

CHAPTER THREE

There still was no pain and Charley dozed off immediately after the C-46 cargo ship took off for Dum Dum Airport in Calcutta 200 miles away. The plane ran into rough weather and Charley was jostled awake several times, although he was strapped to the stretcher and the stretcher was tied down.

It was spring and a Model T Ford stopped in front of the Morris shack. He knew it was spring because his feet no longer were cold when he walked in the creek that ran in front of the shack. He saw, in his dream, the house he lived in. It was gray and it stood on stilts stuck into the clay. He tried to remember who lived there with him. He saw his older brother, Jack, and he tried to peer into the other room of the two-room building. Other kids had fathers and mothers, but when his imagination knocked down a wall so that he could see inside, there was nobody there. He tried to remember his mother, but all he could recall of her was the sound of her crying. As for his father, there never was even the vaguest recollection of him.

Charley was playing with Jack in the clay beneath the shack. He saw the man get out of the Model T and leap the stream. The man walked up the rickety steps and knocked on the door. Charley saw him enter and emerge almost immediately afterwards with a cardboard box. Later, in the car, he saw that the open box contained his and Jack's clothing. Charley was sitting in the front seat beside the man. Jack was in the back.

"How old are you, son?" said the man.

Charley stuck up five fingers.

"How old are you?" said the man, turning to address Jack.

"I'm six years old going on seven," said Jack.

"I'm taking you to a nice place to live," said the man. "You'll like it there. There are lots of boys your ages there."

He heard Jack crying. He turned to look at him, in amazement. Jack was his big brother and he hardly ever cried.

The plane landed and the bump of the wheels on the ground brought him back to the present.

"How you doing, captain?" said a voice.

"I'm okay," he replied, mumbling with swollen lips through the bandages.

"You'll feel better when they get that stuff off you," said the voice.

Later, as if from a distance, he heard another voice. "Hey, down there. We'll need a forklift. We've got a sick man in here. We need a forklift to move him."

The stretcher was carried to the rear of the plane. Charley heard the grinding noise of the forklift. The steel prongs scraped the floor as they dug under the wooden platform on which the stretcher had been placed. Charley was lowered from the plane and he felt himself being placed in another vehicle. Another ambulance, he thought, his senses alert to every movement.

"Take it easy, captain. We'll have you at the Royal Vic in ten minutes. It's the best hospital in this part of the world."

Charley tried to speak but couldn't. He gave a little nod to show that he had heard.

He heard the opening of the ambulance door. The smell of ether and disinfectant entered his mask as he was carried down a corridor.

"Just bring him in here," said a nurse.

"Hello, captain," said a cheerful voice. "My name is Hull. I'm a doctor. I'm going to remove the bandages and take a look at what we have. Just relax. You'll be all right."

When the gauze and tape were stripped away, Charley tried to move his hands and open his eyes. There was no feeling in his hands. He couldn't open his eyes.

"Are you sure the bandages are off?" said Charley, fighting to force his words through lips that were puffing and just beginning to hurt.

"Colonel Hull, Colonel Hull," called the nurse.

"Yes, nurse," said Hull.

"I think he's trying to say something."

"What is it, captain?" asked Hull, and Charley felt his hand on his shoulder.

Charley didn't respond immediately. Suddenly, he had been overtaken with an urgent yearning for water.

"Thirsty," he mumbled. "I'm thirsty."

A steel straw was inserted between his lips. The water tasted of salt. He drank all of it.

"Here, captain," said the nurse. "This will make you feel better."

He felt the sting of a needle as it entered his arm.

Charley and the other boys were standing at the heads of their cots in the dormitory.

"All right, boys" said Miss Wilson, the lady in charge. "Pay attention. I'm going to take you down to the office in a minute to let some nice people look at you. If you act real good, they might take one of you home with them. They can give somebody a very good home. I want you all to act like little gentlemen. Keep your heads up, shoulders back."

Charley liked living at the orphanage. The people were good to him. There was always plenty to eat. They had brown shoes to wear. He and his brother were together. He didn't want to go home with anybody. He put on a small boy's defiance, to frighten away anybody who might want to adopt him. If anybody tried to adopt him, he'd run away and come back to the orphanage.

"That's a good-looking boy there," said a tall skinny man with a funny Adam's apple.

Charley never looked up at these sessions. He slouched over as much as he could without being reprimanded for it in order to present as disagreeable a picture as possible. He didn't want to look up now. The man with the Adam's apple was standing over him.

"Charley Morris," said the lady in charge.

Charley lifted his eyes from the tops of his shoes.

"Don't you want to go home with this nice man?" said the lady.

"No'm," said Charley. "I want to stay here."

Charley went home with the nice man. The man was a policeman and he lived in Birmingham. There were several other children, but only one was young enough for Charley to play with. The policeman's father would visit every weekend and he would always bring a toy to give to the other boy. He never gave Charley anything.

A young woman would check on Charley every three months.

"How do you like living here?" she said every time.

"I don't, ma'm," said Charley. "I want to live with my brother."

He was so happy when she finally took him back to the orphanage that he cried, but his world fell apart when he discovered Jack was no longer there. He had been adopted. Nobody would tell him where he lived. He was only 6, but one day, he figured, he'd be big enough to go and find him.

He heard voices in the room.

"Is he sleeping?" said Colonel Hull.

"Yes," said the nurse. "He went out just after I gave him the needle. How does it look, colonel?"

"Pretty bad, nurse, pretty bad. We're going to have to really fight to keep him alive. Change his bandages every three hours and give him plenty of fluids. Make him drink it even if he resists. He's losing an enormous amount of body fluid through the burned skin. If we don't maintain a proper fluid and chemical balance we'll lose him."

"How about his eyes, doctor? Will he lose his sight?"

"No, I don't think so. The eyelids are badly burned but his eyes seem to be all right. Keep them washed with Boric Acid. Don't be afraid to use plenty of vasoline. It's not important that he won't be able to see for awhile."

Charley lay still. The nurse began removing his bandages, and Charley pretended then to come awake. He murmured something.

"What did you say, captain?" she said, putting her face to his.

"Nothing," he said, pushing out the words one by one,

spacing them so that a truck could drive through the separations, "is going to keep me from going home to Alabama."

"That's right, captain," she said, patting him on the arm.

CHAPTER FOUR

Charley woke to the sound of a Christmas song. A nurse was humming "Silent Night" while she assisted the doctor who was removing his bandages. He always woke when the bandages were changed, sometimes gratefully, when the pain of his nightmares was greater than the hurt of reality. The pain was worse when the gauze glued to dead skin was pulled from his body. He squirmed under the hands of the doctor and nurse.

"Take it easy, captain," said the doctor. "I'll be through in just a minute."

"Merry Christmas, captain," said the nurse, bending over him, looking into his eyes as the wrappings came off his face.

"It's Christmas already?" he asked, seeing her for the first time, now that the mask was gone and ointment wiped away. It was only a glimpse. Her face shimmered away from him as she washed his eyes. It vanished, then, on the other side of the globs of vasoline she applied. Although he had seen before, during the brief periods when the dressings were changed and his eyes were unencumbered, the images that he captured were blurred and distant. That brief look at the nurse's face assured him, in his mind, that his vision had not been damaged. He gave silent thanks to God.

Pushed back into his dark world, now, a strong feeling of relief surged through him. The nurse's bright smile stayed with him, and he was reminded of a girl named Miriam in Alabama. Does she know what happened to me, he wondered.

"Say, nurse, has anybody notified my wife that I'm here?" he asked.

"I'm sure your commanding officer has done that, captain. Just think, you'll be home in a little while and you'll be able to see her. Do you have any children, captain?"

"Just one. A little boy named Freddie. He was born a year ago, just about this time. His birthday and Christmas practically come together."

"That's wonderful, captain. I bet you can't wait to see them."

He heard Colonel Hull addressing him.

"Good morning, captain. How you feeling this Christmas Day?"

"I don't know, colonel. I don't feel much pain, except when the bandages are removed, but I feel weak and tired all the time. I have an idea I'm a lot worse off than I thought."

"I'm going to level with you, captain. You've been badly burned. Some of the burns ran awfully deep. Frankly, you're going to have to have a lot of plastic surgery to rebuild your face. All we can do here is keep you as comfortable as possible. We've got to get you to a first class hospital in the States right away. I'm going to ask the surgeon-general for a Priority One pass for you."

"Thanks, colonel. I want to promise you something. I'm going to make it."

"That's the way to talk, captain. With that attitude,

nothing will stop you."

"If you need anything, captain, just let me know," said the nurse. "I'll be here with you all the time."

"Well," said Colonel Hull, "I'll be leaving you two. I'll drop in from time to time, captain."

Wrapped again inside his silent world, Charley went back to Alabama.

Once again he stood in line in the orphanage office. He was seven and big for his age. A tall, skinny woman walked up and down the line examining the youngsters. Charley kept his head down when Miss Wilson, the matron, wasn't looking in his direction. Occasionally, though, he darted a quick glance at the visitor, hoping she wasn't interested in him.

"They're such nice-looking boys," said the skinny woman. "You've done a wonderful job with them, Miss Wilson. I'd like to take one or two for myself."

Charley shot a look at Miss Wilson and saw that she was beaming proudly. The woman started walking toward him. He dropped his gaze. He felt her presence towering over him.

"Don't take me," he blurted out, suddenly. "I'm not a good boy."

"Oh, Charley, how can you say that?" said the lady in charge. "Don't mind him, Mrs. Allen. Charley Morris is a fine boy. He never gives anybody any trouble.

He was on a train.

"You'll love your new daddy, Charley," said Mrs. Allen. "He's a wonderful man."

"Ain't I going to live with you, ma'am?" said Charley.

"Goodness, no," she said. "I just made the arrangements for Mr. Woods to adopt you. He's going to pick you up in Montgomery."

"Does he have my brother, too?" he asked.

"No, honey," said Mrs. Allen. "Mr. Woods lives with his mother and sister."

"Doesn't Mrs. Woods live with him?" asked Charley.

"There's no Mrs. Woods, honey," she said. "Mr. Woods never married."

"Who's going to boss me around then?"

"Oh, honey," she said, laughing, "there's nobody going to boss you around."

Charley spent the night in Montgomery, in a little room in somebody's house. He didn't know whether it was Mrs. Allen's house or not. The next morning a tall man named P.A. Woods came and got him. Charley liked his face, but he didn't want to go with him.

"I want to go back home," he said, meaning the orphanage.

"Just give us a chance," said Mr. Woods. "If you don't like staying with us after a few days I'll take you back. Okay?"

"All right," said Charley, wiping his eyes and blowing his nose on the handkerchief Mr. Woods handed him.

Charley had been so busy crying that he had not noticed the stout woman who had come with Mr. Woods.

"This is my sister, Annie," said Mr. Woods. "She's going to be your aunt. I want you to call her Aunt Annie."

"All right," said Charley.

"And I want you to call me Daddy," said Mr. Woods.

"All right," said Charley.

As much as he was determined to dislike his new father and everything about him, including the little town of Headland, where he was to live, Charley found it difficult to resist the kindnesses bestowed on him by Mr. Woods, his mother and Aunt Annie. And the neighborhood was crawling

25

with little boys his own age. There were more boys there than in the orphanage.

Charley was standing in the front seat of an abandoned automobile, in a vacant lot, huddled over the steering wheel and making race-car noises, jammed into the vehicle with several of the neighborhood kids. One of the others pulled at his arm.

"Come on, Charley," he said. "It's my turn to drive."

Charley pulled his arm away.

"I hate to do it, captain," said Dr. Hull, "but I've got to get some fresh bandages on you. I'll be as easy on you as I can."

CHAPTER FIVE

His only view of the hospital at Calcutta, the proud
Royal Victoria, was the piece of ceiling he saw when his
bandages were being changed, and then they were only
fleeting glances, before the medication and the new
applications of gauze and tape. Sometimes he saw the face of
the nurse who reminded him of Miriam, Lieutenant Adams.
Time was of no consequence to him. He didn't know whether
he had been in the Royal Vic for a week or a year. It didn't
matter. He became increasingly aware of the whispered
conferences that were held over his bed as doctors probed
and measured him. He trained himself to listen, to catch
some of the hushed comments flowing across his body, while
pretending that he slept.

"He can't last here another month," said one voice. "We
can keep pouring fluid into him while it comes out of all
those burned places, but we can't do that forever. We've got
to get him some place where they can graft skin on him to
keep his fluids in."

"I've asked for a Priority One pass to get him back to
the States," said Colonel Hull's voice. "His orders should be
coming through any time now. I said it was a matter of life or
death."

"Did they believe you? It's always a matter of life or death when somebody wants to get back to the States. I hope they understand it really is this time."

"I explained the whole matter to them. They understand the urgency. My hope is that he can hold on until he gets to a first-class hospital back there. Some hospital where they have the latest techniques for burns and skin-grafting."

"His three hours are up, colonel," said a nurse's voice. "It's time to change bandages."

"Thank you, nurse," said the colonel's voice.

Charley feigned awakening when he started to unravel his mask.

"Hello, captain, how you doing?" said the colonel.

"Tired, colonel. I'm awfully tired all the time. I get the feeling that you're keeping me doped up. Is that right?"

"No, son. You're tired because you're running a continuous fever. That's because your body is fighting to overcome the loss of fluid in your body. The fluid is being leaked out through the burned skin on your hands and face."

"What can we do about it?"

"The main thing for you to do is keep reminding yourself that you're going to go back home to Alabama, like you told me the first day I saw you. If you won't let yourself be whipped, you'll make it. Another thing is I want you to take in all the fluids you can hold. Every time you wake up the nurse will stick a straw in your mouth and I want you to keep sucking on it until you fall asleep again. At the same time we're feeding you fluids through the vein. Just hold on, son. Hold on and we'll make it to Alabama."

"I'll hold on, colonel. Thanks."

"Well, I guess it's time for me to hit the sack," said the

colonel. "Good night, captain. Night, nurse."

"Good night," said Charley.

"Good night, colonel," said the nurse, Lieutenant Adams, who had sat in the chair beside the bed to watch over Charley on her eight-hour shift.

"Here," she told Charley, putting the steel straw in his mouth. "Drink as much as you can."

He sucked on the tube until he heard the gurgling noise signalling the end of the water. He remembered the colonel's urging to drink all the water he could hold.

"Let's go," said Mr. Woods. "We've got to get you in school this morning."

"Please, Mr. Woods," said Charley. "I only just got here."

"Son, you've been here three days already," said Mr. Woods. "And when are you going to start calling me Daddy?"

"Do I have to go to school, Daddy?" said Charley.

"Every child has to go to school," said Mr. Woods. "It's the law."

"That's right," said Aunt Annie. "We'll be in trouble with the law, Charles, if we allowed you to stay out of school."

Charley looked at Mrs. Woods, Mr. Woods' mother.

"Ma'am," he said, "do I have to go to school?"

"I'm afraid so, Charles. There's nothing we can do about it. You've got to go."

"I want to go back to the orphanage," he said.

"Didn't you go to school at the orphanage?" said Aunt Annie. Charley didn't answer.

"Son, I asked you to give us a try, didn't I?" said Mr. Woods. "And didn't you agree?"

"Yes, sir," said Charley, hanging his head. He had never broken a promise and he wasn't going to start now.

He didn't want to admit it to himself, at first, but he liked his new father and Mrs. Woods and Aunt Annie. Even then, wrapped up as he was in the little-boy fun he found in Headland, he wondered about his brother, Jack, and he hoped he was living with good people, too. He remembered dreaming about Jack, but the dreams always ended with Jack walking away from him, waving goodby. He'd call to him. He'd yell for him to stop. Now, reliving the past, he became a boy again and yelled Jack's name.

"What's the matter, captain?" said Lieutenant Adams. He felt her hand on his knee. "Are you all right? Do you want something?"

"No, thanks," he said. "I'm all right. I was just thinking of home."

"Do you want me to give you something so you can sleep?" she asked.

"No, nurse. I'm okay. Thanks."

"Did I hear you say Jack?" she said. "Is there somebody named Jack you want us to contact for you?"

"I wish you could contact him, nurse. The trouble is, I don't know where he is. He's my brother. We were separated when we were kids."

He heard the door open and steps approached his bed.

"I've got some good news, captain," said Colonel Hull. "Your orders just came through. We're going to put you on the plane for the States in a few hours. I didn't want to disturb you, but I thought you'd want to know about this."

"Thanks, colonel. I'm grateful for all you've done for me."

"That's all right, son. Now, listen. It's going to be a

rough trip back to the States. You're going to have to stop a few times along the way so that you can be cleaned up and treated. Those bandages have to be changed. You've got a Priority One pass. That means nobody can bump you. In fact, with that pass you can bump practically anybody else. You're cleared all the way through, so there's no problem. Now I want you to pay strict attention to what I say. Can you hear me? Do you understand?"

"Yes, sir. I'm listening."

"All right. When you get back to the States, Army regulations require that an injured person be sent to the medical facility closest to his home. You're from Alabama and there's a fine hospital in Tuscaloosa. They'll probably want to send you there. But I don't want you to go to Tuscaloosa, captain. You understand? The best facilities for burn patients are at the Valley Forge General Hospital near Philadelphia. That's where I want you to go. I've made that recommendation on your orders. I don't know how much good my recommendation will do. It's up to you, captain. Every chance you get, I want you to ask to go to Valley Forge. That's your best chance, captain. Keep raising hell until they send you to Valley Forge. Okay, captain?"

"Okay, colonel. Valley Forge General Hospital. I'll remember that, and I promise you, colonel, that I'll get there."

"I know you will, son. I know you will. Good luck."

CHAPTER SIX

At first, when he was told he was going home, he saw himself getting off the plane in Dothan and rushing to sweep Miriam and Freddie up in his arms, swinging them in the joy of homecoming. He saw himself as he used to be, straight, tall and proud, all features intact, happily smiling with lips that were whole.

Locked up in his private world, closed off from everyone except doctors and nurses, Charley Woods remembered only the photographs of what he had been. There was one, his latest picture, that Miriam said she showed to Freddie every day, so that he would know his daddy when he saw him.

"What were you thinking about when it was taken, Charley?" said Miriam. "What were you laughing about."

He smiled to himself inside his mask, remembering, and it came to him, then, that Miriam would not recognize him now, and Freddie would have to get a new photograph of him to memorize.

Charley put together the bits of muffled conversation he heard by those who ministered to him, who had no way of knowing whether he was asleep or awake, and, sometimes, from the tones of their voices, he realized that there were some who talked of him as though he were already dead.

From the daily ritual of removing the dead, charred skin, he knew that his hair and scalp would be gone. He would lose his ears. His nose and lips would have to be rebuilt. His eyelids, too, would have to be reconstructed. His hands were numb and he wondered if he would lose them.

What would Miriam think about the new Charley Woods? He recalled seeing a movie once, "The Phantom of the Opera," where a man who had been a star lived in the hidden, underground rooms of an opera house in Paris. He fell in love with the heroine of the picture, who was a singer, and one day he lured her to his underground world. Either he or she removed his mask, Charley couldn't remember exactly, and the girl screamed in terror when she saw his face. He had been scarred in a fire long before. Would Miriam scream when she saw him?

Charley was being wheeled out of the room. The cart stopped.

"I just want to say good-by and wish you luck, captain," said Colonel Hull. "Do you remember what I told you?"

"Yes, sir. Valley Forge General Hospital."

"Good. Well, I'll be seeing you."

"Say, colonel, how long have I been here?"

"This is your twelfth day, captain. How long did you think you were here?"

"I had no idea, sir. The days kept bumping into each other, and I never knew when one day ended and another began."

"Well, God bless you, son."

"God bless you, too, colonel."

Charley was lifted by a forklift truck to the rear door of

the C-46 cargo plane. He felt himself being raised from the pallet. He was carried to a rack on the side of the fuselage and strapped down.

"Hello," said a woman's voice, "I'm a nurse. I'm going with you, all the way to the States."

"What's your name?" said Charley. Although still difficult, he was able to speak better now.

"Lieutenant Marie DesChesne," she said, spelling it for him. "I'm in the Army."

"Who's going with us, lieutenant?"

"About 30 in all, including the crew. The others are American, British and Indian soldiers."

"I'm going to take your temperature now," she said, placing a thermometer in his mouth.

He heard the door bang shut and the heat and stuffiness closed in on him. She removed the thermometer.

"How high is it?" he gasped. He knew it was high. It was always high. He had heard the doctors talking about how difficult it was to break his fever.

"Don't worry, captain," said Lieutenant DesChesne. "I'm going to take good care of you."

The engines started and Charley relaxed. He knew the plane soon would be cool. The nurse turned the small air vents on him.

"Thanks, lieutenant," he said, and he realized how grateful he had become for little things.

Just before the plane left the runway, Charley breathed his usual prayer.

"Dear God, please be with us," he said.

He always said it on take-off, and he wondered how many fliers there were who asked God's help. Probably all of them, he told himself, whether they admitted it or not.

In the cool air of the plane, Charley's eyes became dry. With eyelids so damaged they couldn't function, he could not blink to keep his eyes moist. He recalled the regular routine at the Royal Vic. Nurses were forever piling vasoline on his eyes.

"We've got to do it, captain," Lieutenant Adams had explained one night, when he complained because he could not see. "Otherwise, they'll dry up and develop ulcers."

He tried to tell Lieutenant DesChesne that his eyes should be treated with vasoline. She could not understand him above the roar of the plane, and he didn't have the strength to make his voice heard.

The pain that he knew one day would come, and which he had gratefully eluded so far, now began making its presence known. It was there all the time, waiting for the propitious time to strike. It arrived with each dip and swerve of the aircraft. Hot bullets entered his brain when the plane jostled his head on the pillow. There was no escaping. The slightest movement filled his head with hurting.

He tried to will the pain away by thinking of happier times. He had returned to Alabama in February, 1943, after transferring to the U.S. Air Corps, now that America was positive there was a war, and he married his sweetheart from Hartford, only a few miles from Dothan. Miriam Wilkes. She was 20 and he was 21. He thought he'd had his share of fighting. He had fought with the Canadians in North Africa, and he figured he and Miriam would wait out the war on some safe American base.

Before going to North Africa, he had been stationed in England, and the Britons, all of them, were a people at war. They labored in support of the national effort to bring the bluebirds back to the white cliffs of Dover. There were no

40-hour weeks in England, nor on any of the fighting fronts. Charley, who knew what war was, and who had seen dying, resented the daily 5 o'clock trek to the officers' club, a ritual at the end of the day's work, and he couldn't understand why troops based in America had the weekends off, while others were working and fighting every day around the clock.

Charley Woods was not an officers' club soldier. He asked to be transferred overseas.

"I can't fight a war this way, Miriam," he said. "I can't stay here and enjoy myself while my friends are fighting and maybe dying. I've got to go back."

"All right, Charley. I understand."

That's the way Miriam is, he thought. She wasn't the wife of an officers' club soldier.

As the C-46 droned on toward Karachi, Charley followed a different route, from Alabama to Kurmitola, India, where he took up quarters in a jungle tent beside a makeshift air field. He was lucky. He had lost only one tent mate. He thought of Ralph Keele, his devil-may-care buddy. While other pilots vanished from the tents around them, lost with their B-24 tankers of gasoline in the valleys of the Hump, Charley and Ralph led charmed lives. They always came back. He wondered where Ralph was now. They flew the Hump seven days a week, most times with only five or six hours of sleep, snatching some of the precious rest under the wings in China while the gasoline was being unloaded. He wondered how the flight surgeon was making out in his fight to get the crewmen more sack time. He complained so much that the commanding officer issued a directive. Pilots must have eight hours on the ground before flying again. Charley smiled at that, remembering how the operations people had got around that.

"Hey, Charley," Ralph Keele had said, "did you see how operations handled that eight-hour business?"

"No, Ralph. How did they get around it? I figured they would, anyway."

"They count the eight hours from the time your plane hits the ground. Ain't that great? That means after we're through with all the paper work, aircraft checks and briefings, we might be able to squeeze in four hours of shut-eye."

"What's the doctor say about that?"

"He says he's going to complain higher up. He's so mad he could spit nails."

Charley and Ralph didn't spend much time together in their tent. They never flew together. When one was coming in the other was going out.

Another memory wedged its way in. Sleeping under the wing of a plane on a Chinese runway required a lot of practice.

The runways and taxi strips were built of broken rocks, and the thousands of Chinese workers were too busy to concern themselves with making them comfortable for sleeping. Charley recalled how the jagged rocks cut into his back and sides.

Charley was lucky in another regard. He had never killed a native when he came in for a landing. The native Chinese believed devils were following them. They would dash in front of a landing plane in the hope the craft would destroy the demons behind them, timing their mad sprints so that they would narrowly miss the whirling propeller blades. The insane scramble occured at every landing, in spite of the frantic efforts of armed soldiers to keep them off the field. Prior to landing on a Chinese field, Charley would radio ahead: "We're coming in. Please clear the natives off the field." They were always there, though, breaking through the lines of the armed soldiers, to run their race with death. Some lost the race.

He tried not to think of his crew, Hoag, Rodriguez, and Stalmacher, but once again he saw Stalmacher flailing the fire on his chest, and Hoag and Rodriguez, comrades of many flights, rode into his mind on flames. He cried out.

"What's the matter, captain?" said the nurse, touching his shoulder. "Are you all right?"

Charley nodded.

"Try to rest, captain. We'll be there in less than two hours. Can I do anything for you?"

Charley shook his head. He mumbled something.

"What did you say, captain? I can't hear you."

"I said I'm going to make it," he said.

"I know you will, captain," she said, echoing the words of Colonel Hull.

CHAPTER SEVEN

Exhausted, physically and mentally, Charley was asleep when the plane landed in Karachi. He woke to the sound of many voices. A nurse was unwinding his bandages. Another placed vasoline on his eyes. Doctors conferred in low voices.

"What time is it?" he asked. He wondered after he said it why he was always asking somebody the time.

"Oh, you're awake," said a nurse. "Welcome to Karachi. It's 2 o'clock. Why? You planning to go somewhere?"

"Morning or afternoon?"

"Afternoon, captain. I guess you've had a rough trip. Take it easy. You'll be all right now."

"How long will I have to stay here?"

This time a doctor answered.

"Hello, captain. I'm Major Tompkins. I'll be your doctor while you're here. You should be ready to travel again in three or four days.

The nurse and the major had English accents.

"Is this a British hospital?" asked Charley.

"That's right, captain. Of course, we've got some American personnel here, too."

Just as the Royal Vic, Charley's wounds were cleaned and dressed frequently. His eyes were washed and covered

39

with vasoline. Doctors maintained a constant check of his chemical body balance, making certain that he took in enough fluids to offset the tremendous losses through his burned skin.

Here he was in Karachi, and one day, if the subject ever came up, he could always say he had visited there.

"Oh, isn't that marvelous. And what did you see?"

"Nothing," he would reply.

He wondered how many other exotically-named places he would visit and never see, on this flight across the world that he knew was a flight for survival.

He was standing in front of his house on stilts and he saw a bulky object float down the swollen stream that separated the shack from the dirt road.

"Hey," he yelled at Jack. "Come see what's in the water."

They raced to the water's edge. They saw a dead goat go floating by.

His brother left him there, staring at the drowned animal, turning several times to wave good-by. He wondered where he was going.

"Hey, come back," he yelled. "Come back. I'm all alone."

Jack faded from view.

"Well, captain," said the British doctor, "it's time for you to continue on your way. Your condition has stabilized very well. The plane is ready to take you to Cairo.

Marie DeChesne was waiting in the plane.

"Where you from, Marie?" said Charley, making conversation while the engines were warming up.

"Pennsylvania," she said. "New Hope, Pennsylvania. Ever hear of it?"

"No," said Charley. "Never did. Do you know anything about the Valley Forge General Hospital?"

"I know all about Valley Forge, but I never heard of a hospital there. Is that where you're going?"

"Yes." he said, with flagging spirits. Why did Colonel Hull think it was such a wonderful hospital if nobody ever heard of it?

Again, the movement of the plane pushed his head from side to side, sending bolts of excrutiating pain through him.

"Dear God, please be with us," he said as the plane sailed down the runway. He added, "God, please help ease my pain."

The pain became unbearable as the craft battled the wind currents. He called to the nurse. She put her face to his head.

"Can you give me something to make me sleep?" he said, asking for the relief of a drug for the first time.

"Certainly, captain," she said. She pushed a needle into his arm.

He wakened to the strange sound of silence. The plane had landed.

"Where are we?" he asked.

"Welcome to Basra, captain," said Marie. "We're just stopping here for fuel. We'll be on our way in a few minutes."

"Where's Basra?" he said.

"It's in Iraq, I think," she said.

Charley was lifted off the plane and taken to an infirmary, where doctors and nurses worked over him again. He was given a shot of penicillin. While a nurse spoon-fed him a diet of tasteless soft food, bandages were changed.

It was later, while he was being wheeled back to the

plane that he heard somebody calling out his name.

"Charley? Charley Woods? Is that you?"

He recognized the voice of his commanding officer, Colonel Cannon.

"Colonel Cannon. What are you doing here?"

"I'm in Basra waiting for a hop, Charley. I'm going to the States, too. I heard you were on board and I wanted to see you before I left."

"Are you being transferred, colonel?"

"No, Charley. It's my son. He was taking off in a P-38 in Cleveland when a tire blew out. It ran into some heavy equipment. I'm going home for the funeral."

"I'm sorry, colonel. What can I say?"

"I know, Charley. I know."

"Say, colonel, I hate to ask you, with your son on your mind, but did any of my crew get out of that plane?"

"No, Charley. You were the only one to make it out. Well, Charley, good luck. I hope we run into each other again sometime."

"Same here, colonel. I'm sorry about your boy."

The C-46 headed for the runway.

Charley calculated the time it would take the slow C-46 to reach Cairo. It was about 1100 miles from Basra, he had been told, and he reckoned the flying time at five and a half hours. The plane taxied onto the runway, and, without waiting for clearance from the tower, turned onto the strip with one fluid motion and roared into the wind and took off. His pilot's mind clicked. The doctors had not detained him at Basra because it was imperative to get him on his way immediately. Every second counted. Obviously, the pilot had been given instructions to take off as soon as he reached the runway.

The pain increased. It spread from his head to his shoulders and arms. The heat, fever, sweat, bandages, straps, all began to take a drastic toll. He fought the desire for the relief of a drugged sleep. He would not ask for the needle. He would not become dependent on dope. There was only one way to fight back, with his mind. He endeavored to escape the present by forcing himself to concentrate on brighter times.

"Are you all right?" asked Marie DesChesne. "Want something to put you to sleep?"

He shook his head and wrestled for the beginning of a happy memory.

He remembered his first experience behind the controls of a Curtiss C-46. He was a lieutenant then, a flying instructor, and the operations officer had driven him out to the big plane in a jeep.

"This is a C-46," he said, "and these are your students. Give them some instructions."

He looked at the plane, and he glanced at two young, eager cadets.

He recalled a story told by his commanding general, General William Turner, at one of his classes.

"I was ordered to get into a plane one day and fly it, even though I had never been checked out on it," said the general. "What made it worse, I had to fly a load of passengers. I vowed right then and there that no man in my command would ever have to fly a plane unless he was properly checked out."

Charley wondered whether the operations officer had heard that speech by General Turner. Anyway, orders were orders. He sat in the co-pilot's seat and let the new fliers take turns in the pilot's seat. Luckily, the young cadets already had logged some time in a C-46 and when the instruction was over Charley had learned more from the students than they had learned from him.

"Golly," said one of them after they landed, "I'll be glad when I have as many hours in that bird as you do. You really know how to fly that thing."

Charley wondered what had happened to those two boys. The last he saw of them, they were assigned to one of the squadrons carrying gasoline over the Hump from India to China. Were they still hanging in there?

The hours dragged on. He slipped in and out of consciousness. Sometimes, he didn't know whether he was dreaming or remembering.

In school in Headland, Charley was in and out of trouble, mostly in. Daddy Woods had gone to California. His grandmother, Mrs. Woods, and Aunt Annie sat in rocking chairs and stared at him with grim faces.

"Charley," Aunt Annie said, "I think it's time you had a change of environment. You're ten years old. You're getting to be a big boy. We're going to send you to live with your father in California."

Aunt Annie put him on the train, shook his hand and patted him clumsily on the shoulder. He could see that she had the look of somebody who was about to cry. A lady from the Traveler's Aid tied a cardboard label to his lapel. It said "Charles Wood, in care of Mrs. Amie Howard, 26 Elm Street, Los Angeles, Calif."

"That's in case you get lost," she explained.

When he read the label and saw "Los Angeles" Charley tried to disguise his delight as he bade his aunt good-by.

Wow, he thought, Los Angeles. That's where all those movie stars are. Maybe I'll get to meet some of them.

44

Daddy Woods and Mrs. Howard met him at the station. Mrs. Howard was such a nice, pleasant woman that Charley promised himself to behave. But he didn't, and he didn't meet any movie stars, not that trip, anyway. Reluctantly, Daddy Woods shipped Charley back to Headland as soon as he got out of school in Hollywood, Grant Grammer School. From then on, it seemed, he was constantly on the move as Daddy Woods tried to find a place that could hold him and tame him. He went to Georgia for a spell. He went to Los Angeles twice more. He spent the seventh and eighth grades in LeComte Junior High in Hollywood, the ninth grade in Headland, and the tenth grade in Hollywood High, where he used to see Judy Garland and Lana Turner in the corridor. Hey, Judy Garland was in his French class. He finished high school in Headland.

He smiled in his reverie, despite the throbbing pain, and he wished there were some way for the Woods' to know how grateful he was to them for their patience and kindness.

The hurt was gone, and Charley bumped into Judy Garland as he walked around a corner in Dothan, Alabama.

"Hi, Judy," he said. "What are you doing here in Dothan?"

"Hi, Charley," she said. "We're having a premiere of my new picture here. Didn't you know that?"

"In Dothan?" he said, incredulously.

"That's right, Charley," she said, looking down with those big brown eyes. "I knew you were from around here. We're going to have one premiere in Dothan and another one in Headland."

"Gosh, Judy, I didn't know you felt that way about me."

"Didn't you wonder why I made such terrible grades in

French, Charley? It was my worst subject."

"I just didn't know, Judy."

"Well, you would have known if you had taken your eyes off Lana Turner once in awhile."

Judy started singing and the people of Dothan turned to stare at her.

"Don't," said Charley. "Come on, Judy, quit it."

CHAPTER EIGHT

When Charley woke, he knew he had made it to Cairo, at least. He lay in a fresh bed. His bandages were clean. He didn't know that all through the night, after he had been carried unconscious from the plane, doctors and nurses had worked to save him. He had been given transfusions and medications to bring his body fluids and chemicals back to balance. His eyes had been washed with a solution of Boric Acid and packed with vasoline. For the first time in days, he felt cool and safe.

"How are you feeling, son? My name is Joel Weinberg. I'm a doctor."

"I'm all right, doctor. It's the best I've felt in a long time."

"Well, take it easy, son. We'll get you in shape for the next leg of your trip. You'll be seeing a lot of me before you take off again."

"Say doctor, what place is this. I mean, is this a civilian hospital."

"It's the 38th General Hospital in Cairo, a military hospital. My full name, if you're puzzled, is Captain Joel Weinberg, United States Army Reserves. You can say I'm a civilian on temporary duty in the Army."

"Okay, captain. Thanks. I just didn't know what to call you, that's all."

"Call me whatever you like, son, but don't forget to call me if you need anything."

Charley's fluid levels were maintained. He was slated to stay a week in Cairo, and doctors built up his strength with whole blood, penicillin and soft foods. Since he was still being spoon-fed, the food had no taste, because he could not see it. On his second day, realizing the need for taking in all the water he could hold, Charley vomited much of the liquid. With fluids escaping through the burned areas, the vomiting kept his fluid levels low. He became feverish and grew sicker than he'd been.

"Doctor," said a nurse, "he's vomiting his liquids."

"Well," said the doctor, a strange voice to him, not Captain Weinberg's, "just take him off liquids."

Charley heard the death sentence with terror. Without water he would die. All that day he begged the nurse for water.

"Sorry," she said. "No fluids. Doctor's orders."

Later, Captain Weinberg visited him.

"How are you feeling, son?" he asked.

Charley's tongue had swollen so that he couldn't speak. The mask was off, and he showed the doctor his tongue.

"You need water, son. Nurse, give this boy some fluids."

He left the room. The nurse refused to give him a drink. All Charley wanted then was just strength enough to strangle her. The no-water doctor apparently out-ranked Captain Weinberg.

His tongue filled his mouth. He was ripping at the plexiglass window again, fighting to get out of the stricken plane. It crashed and he was crawling across a desert in search of water. He saw a lake and flung himself into it. His mouth drank sand. He heard Captain Weinberg's voice, as though from a far place.

"Didn't I leave orders to give this boy some fluids?"

The soft, gentle voice was angry.

"We had instructions to take him off fluids," said the nurse.

"I don't give a damn what instructions you got. Give him some water, and give him fluids whenever he wants them. That's an order."

Charley still threw up most of the water, but he drank enough of it to keep his fluid count at a not so precarious level.

He had been in Cairo a week when Captain Weinberg told Charley it was time for him to go.

"Captain, I don't think I can last another day in the C-46," he said. "I just can't take that bumpy ride."

"I don't know anything about flying, son. What's so different about that plane?"

"Well, captain, it's this way. The C-46 flies at a low altitude and that hot air coming off the desert pushes it all over the place. I'd just as soon wait here until a C-54 comes through here. That's a big plane and it flies way up there. It can get away from the wind drafts."

"Let me see what I can do. Let me go make some calls."

"No kidding, captain. You'll be killing me if you send me out on that C-46."

"I'll be right back, son," said Weinberg. "Don't go away."

Charley heard him re-enter the room.

"I waved that Priority One at them, son," he said.

49

"They're sending a C-54 from Casablanca to pick you up. It's leaving this morning. It will be here in a couple of days."

"You mean the Air Corps is sending a plane 4,000 miles just for me?" said Charley. "I don't believe it."

Two days later, early in the morning, Charley was loaded onto the C-54 and the big plane headed back to Casablanca. It gave Charley a smoother ride, but there still was the pain that came when, before the C-54 reached a high cruising level, the air currents bumped the craft and bounced his head on the pillow. Yet, it was a lower plateau of pain than he had experienced in the C-46. Whether a lower or higher plateau of pain, pain was pain, and Charley psyched himself into believing that he would not die.

"You're going to make it, Charley," he told himself. "You're going to make it. You're going home to Alabama. Hold on, Charley, hold on."

"Where's he going?" he heard someone say. "He's never flown this thing this high before."

Charley gave silent thanks to Dr. Weinberg and the pilot. He figured Weinberg had told the pilot about Charley's discomfort at lower heights.

Yet, even when the plane had leveled off, Charley's pain continued. He knew there was a long way to go before the first stop in Libya, having flown the route when he was with the R.A.F., and he asked Marie for something to ease the pain. She gave him a shot of morphine.

Afterwards, he chided himself for surrendering to the urge for drugged relief, but the pain had gone, and he rationalized that the medicine brought him one step closer to Alabama. When he rebuked himself, however, Charley conceded in his secret heart that the self-chastisement came at a time when he felt no hurt. It's easy to condemn the use of morphine for the alleviation of suffering when you don't need it. The drug was beginning to wear off when they landed in Libya. An hour's stop was scheduled for refueling. Charley was transferred to the base hospital for treatment and re-bandaging. For the first time, Charley became conscious of the rank odor of his dead and rotting skin, and he marvelled that the two doctors working on him could maintain a steady, pleasant chatter.

Back on the plane, Charley told himself that he would fight the pain in his own way, with his mind, without succumbing to a request for morphine.

"Well, captain," said Marie, just before take-off, "you want me to give you another shot? If I give it to you now maybe you'll be able to sleep the rest of the way."

"No thanks," he said. "I won't be needing that anymore."

He put his mind to work. He thought of Miriam. There were other girls before he met Miriam, on January 3, 1941. He even remembered the date. In fact, he could recall the exact time and the place. It was 8 o'clock in Hartford, Alabama. She was a blind date. Johnny Wilcox arranged the date and introduced them.

"Charley," said Johnny, "I want you to meet Miriam Wilkes."

He looked down at the pretty little thing from his height of six feet. Miriam was no bigger than a minute. He looked into laughing eyes of blue and capitulated. This was the girl for him.

"Where you from?" he said.

"Hartford," she said. "I'm from right here."

"Why, this is just around the corner from where I live. How come I haven't seen you around?"

"Maybe you weren't looking," she said.

He was 19 and she was 18, but there was no doubt in Charley's mind that one day he would take this girl to be his lawful wedded wife.

Charley courted her assiduously, never missing a day. They would marry and Charley would open his own garage, but the war in strange, foreign places was heating up.

"Look, honey," he said, "I might have to get into that thing. We're all going to be in it."

"Shoot, Charley," said Miriam, "you know President Roosevelt's not going to let us get into that war. Didn't he say that no American boys would fight on foreign land? Well, you know nobody's going to come over here to fight us."

"That guy Adolph Hitler has gone too far already, Miriam. He's going to get the whole world involved. If we're going to stop him, we have to start now."

"Well, Charley, why don't you wait until America gets in it, although I don't think that's ever going to happen? I think you just like the idea of travelling. Everytime somebody turns around you're either going to California or some other place."

"Now, honey, you know that's not right. I haven't left Dothan since I came back from Los Angeles a year ago. You know that's the truth."

"It's time for you to move again, then. I don't think you ever stayed in one place more than a year."

"I've got to go, Miriam," he said, gathering her in his arms. He stroked her long dark hair.

"All right, Charley," she said, mumbling the words, her head against his shoulder. "All right."

Charley traveled by bus to Windsor, Ontario, and enlisted in the Royal Canadian Air Force. Although only 19,

Charley was accepted. Canada was in the war and needed all the men she could find.

Basic training was a snap for the lean, lithe Alabama boy. There, at Trenton, Ontario, he met two other Americans who had joined the Canadians, Len Morgan and Bill Baldwin. In later months, after they had won their wings and had been scattered around the world, Charley would run into Len or Bill in some part of the globe none of them had heard of before. Their only lasting memory of their training days was the night when two men and a young pregnant girl drove up to the gate in Trenton. Charley was on guard duty, as it happened.

"We want to see the commanding officer," said the older of the two men.

"What do you want to see him about, sir?" said Charley.

"We'll tell him," he said.

Charley telephoned headquarters and communicated the request, which, in retrospect, was more than that. It was a command.

Later, the recruits were ordered to stand in line. As they stood there, the girl walked down the line, reviewing the troops.

"That's him," she said, pointing to a young man who stood shrinking in the rear.

"Are you sure?" said the older man.

"That's him," she said. "I could never forget him."

Afterwards, Charley learned the Canadians had come to Trenton in search of the man who had fathered the girl's unborn child. He never knew the end of the story. The accused boy disappeared the following day.

"The poor guy," said Charley, when he told the

story to Miriam, who was somewhat less sympathetic.

"What do you mean, poor guy?" she snapped. "What about the girl? That poor guy should have been horse-whipped."

Charley received his wings at Alymer Flying School in November and was ordered to England, his duty to start in 14 days. This gave him 10 days to spend with Miriam.

"We'll get married after this tour," he said.

"Why not now?" she said.

"Honey, I'm going to England in a few days. I can't marry you and then run off to some foreign country. Wait till I get back."

"Okay, Charley. I'll wait."

He flew cargo planes in North Africa and served as test pilot in East Africa. He was now flying for the Royal Air Force, the Canadian unit having been absorbed by the mother group. Then, when America entered the war, Charley and the other Americans were transferred to the U.S. Army Air Corps. Two months later, in February, 1942, he flew a B-24 from Casablanca to an American base in Brazil, then on to Dallas, Texas. Given a two-week leave of abscence, he went home to Dothan and married Miriam.

"You've had enough war," she said. "Now you can stay home and take care of me."

"You're right, honey. A year of war is enough for any man. Somebody else can take my place over there."

He told her, now that he was safe and could laugh about them, that he once crash-landed in the desert, when a Turkish plane he was flying ran out of fuel and, on another occasion, how he nearly cracked up in a C-47 loaded with British soldiers.

"I was ferrying them from Casablanca to Khartoum,"

he said. "I thought I'd never get it off the ground. I was reaching the end of the runway and was going too fast to stop. Finally, I just managed to lift her up and barely got over some bushes at the end of the runway. Once in the air, I couldn't get the plane to climb. I nursed that thing and managed to get it up to 10,000 feet. I had to keep fighting the controls to keep her up that high. I asked the co-pilot to take over while I checked to see if there was something wrong with the plane."

"What did you find, Charley?" Miriam had said, dreamily, her head on his shoulder, no fear of danger now that the danger was past.

"My passengers were sleeping on the floor," he said, drawing out the story. "I had to step over and around them while I checked the inside of the plane. The wings were okay. There was nothing wrong with the craft. I went to the baggage compartment. The lunkhead who had loaded the plane had left 2,000 pounds of sand bags, ballast, on board. He had tied the soldiers' baggage on top of it. The ballast had been put on her because the plane had come in empty. That was to weight it down. It should have been removed before we took on a maximum load of passengers and gasoline."

Miriam had fallen asleep.

"Hey," he said, shaking her awakd. "I'm telling you about my war adventures."

"Oh," she said, looking up at his face, smiling, "I thought you finished that story." What happened in the sky over Africa was something that occurred in another world, and nothing had happened, anyway, since Charley was home and safe. "Go ahead, I'm listening."

"That's what I'm going to do, whether you're listening or not," he said. "I went back to the cockpit and told the radio operator about the sand bags. We went back to the baggage section, opened the back door and threw out the ballast, bag by bag. The passengers were sitting up looking at us. We finished unloading the ballast and they went back to sleep. They probably had figured that throwing sand bags out of a plane at 10,000 feet was routine practice."

Miriam, too, had gone back to sleep.

He grinned at that, behind his mask, or thought he was grinning. His lips were dead. Charley could open his mouth but he couldn't twist his lips.

He was weak, tired and thirsty. He was soaked by the fluids held by the bandages. The C-54 was circling the Casablanca field, and Charley realized he had stopped most of the pain by brute force of will.

CHAPTER NINE

In Casablanca, Charley was moved into a ward. He knew it was a ward because there were patients on each side of him. Doctors and nurses followed the same routine he remembered from Calcutta and Cairo. Every three hours his bandages were removed. The wounds were cleaned, the dead skin stripped off, his eyes washed and treated, and the bandages were replaced.

"How long will I be here?" he asked a nurse.

"About a week," she said.

She was cool and distant, not like the other nurses he had encountered along the way, except, of course, for the nurse who wouldn't give him water, and he supposed it was because there were other patients in the ward who required her attention.

"I need plenty of water," he said. "Will you be here to give it to me when I need it?"

"There's an orderly here," she said. "Just let him know when you're thirsty."

"Miss," he said, becoming irritated at her manner, "I don't have the strength to yell."

"All right, captain," she said. "I'll tell him to check with you every so often."

After the nurse left, the orderly came to his bed.

"I'm the orderly here, captain," he said. "My name is Henry Daley. Anything you want just whistle."

"Could I have some water?" said Charley.

The orderly held a straw to his mouth.

"Okay?" said Daley after Charley had emptied the glass.

"Okay, thanks," said Charley.

"Hi," said the patient on Charley's right. "How you doing?"

"I'm all right," said Charley.

"Name's Joe Willoughby," said the other. "Got a foot blown off. What happened to you?"

"Plane blew up on take off," said Charley.

"Tough luck, man. Well, one thing you can say about it, the war's over for us."

In the ensuing days, while being prepared for his trip across the Atlantic, Charley learned that Joe Willoughby was from Wigan, England, that he was an infantryman and that he had lost his foot to a land mine.

The patient in the bed to Charley's left never spoke to anyone. He was British, too. He had seen his comrades slaughtered in a trap, and when he was found, unable to tell his rescuers anything, he was wandering in the desert.

It hurt Charley to speak, and he spoke very little. Most of the time he slept.

Charley was preparing to board his Liberator for another hop across the Hump. Ralph Keele, his tent mate, pulled up in a jeep.

"Hey, Charley, wait a minute. There's somebody here wants to see you."

It was his brother. He recognized him immediately. He had the same face he remembered as a boy.

"Jack, where did you come from?"

"I heard you were over here and I just dropped in. I've been looking everywhere for you."

"Me, too, Jack. Nobody knew where you went. Say, I'm just going to deliver a load of gas. Why don't you come along? You can be my co-pilot."

"That's a good idea, Charley. I brought my gear along just in case."

Charley saw that he was wearing a flight jacket.

"Where we headed, Charley?" said Jack as the plane left the runway. Charley noticed the motors were running quiet, and Jack wasn't even raising his voice. Usually, you had to yell to be heard in the cockpit of the big plane.

"To a little place in China called Lulaing. I'm delivering gas to the Flying Tigers."

"Hey, that's great. I always wanted to meet some of those guys. Maybe I'll get to meet General Chennault."

"That's no problem, Jack. I'll introduce you when we get to Lulaing."

The majestic peaks of the Himalayas rose before them. Charley lifted the nose and took the plane up to 19,000 feet.

"The idea, Jack," he explained, "is to get above the lower peaks. This way, you can find your way easy enough through the high ones."

"Those mountains sure look pretty, Charley. Look at all that snow. How about going down a little so I can make me a snowball?"

Charley took the plane to the side of the mountain. Jack reached out the window and grabbed a handful of snow.

"This is more snow than I've seen in Alabama all winter," said Jack, laughing. "I think I'll put it in a package and send it home."

"Is that where you're living now, Jack, Alabama? Where, Jack? I swear I've looked all over that state for you. Shucks, I'm living in Dothan. It's a wonder we never ran into each other."

In the distance, on the China side of the Hump, the stars were blinking.

"Hey, Charley, look. The stars are winking at us. How about that?"

"Those are Japanese fighter planes, Jack. Every time you see stars blinking in succession that means a Jap plane went under them."

"Well, I'll be dogged," said Jack. "There must be a hundred planes out there, then. Aren't you worried they'll see us?"

"It wouldn't be a bad idea to get into some cover, Jack. Let's go down and get in a cloud."

"Hey, that was neat, Charley. Now I can't see any stars at all."

"They'll be gone by the time we pass over Tibet," said Charley. "Then it's just a little way into Lulaing."

"Say, Charley, I hate to think of you flying these mountains every day. It looks like mighty dangerous work to me."

"I know, Jack, but somebody has to deliver the gas to the Flying Tigers."

"Don't forget, Charley. You said you'd introduce me to General Chennault."

The plane dropped out of the mountain range and headed for the plains of China.

"What's down there, Charley?" said Jack.

"Oh, that's a Japanese outpost. Want to see it?"

"I sure would. Can we get close enough to see the

people or would it be too dangerous?" Jack asked.

Charley dropped the plane to 200 feet.

"Look at them running down there," said Jack. "They must think you're going to bomb them."

General Chennault met the plane as it landed.

"Hi, Charley," he said. "Have any trouble getting here?"

"No, sir," said Charley, "it was clear sailing all the way. We saw some Japanese fighters over to the south and we ducked into some clouds."

"Who's this young fellow with you, Charley?"

"Oh, this is my brother. I brought him over to meet you. Jack, this is General Chennault."

"It's nice meeting you, Jack, your brother has been telling me all about you."

"Same here, sir. Say, general, how do I go about joining the Flying Tigers?"

"Just come with me, Jack. I'm always looking for good men. You can command one of my squadrons."

General Chennault and Jack walked away from the plane. The general had his arm around Jack's shoulders. They went out of Charley's sight.

"Hey, Jack," yelled Charley. "Hey, Jack, wait."

He jumped into the seat of a fighter plane that was parked at the edge of the field and started searching for Jack and General Chennault. Somehow, he found himself on the Indian side of the Himalayas, and a driving snowstorm tossed the little craft from side to side in a valley of the Hump. He came down close to the ground, and the snow was gone, and Charley landed on a flat place in a range of hills. He realized he was far off course and that he was in the Naga Hills, the land of the head hunters. He jumped out of the plane and was surrounded by fierce-faced natives wearing tattered peasant clothing. They carried spears and long knives. He felt for his money belt, which all pilots carried. It was gone, and with it the rupees to be used to buy his way back to an Allied base.

Charley was pushed and pulled and kicked to a village lined with grass shacks. At the edge of the village, he saw a row of heads stuck on the top of tall poles. One head was familiar. It was his. He broke away from his tormentors and ran screaming into the jungle. He didn't stop screaming until an orderly shook him awake.

"Stop it, captain. Stop it. There are other patients in the building, you know. You're keeping them all awake."

"Okay," said Charley, realizing where he was. "I'll try to watch it."

"That's good, captain," said the orderly, who apparently believed a man could control his nightmares.

He remembered now, in that interval between pain and sleep, that he had seen a picture of the heads of six young men affixed to poles in a Naga village. It had been taken by a downed pilot, who only thirty minutes earlier had snapped a photograph of six youths from a neighboring tribe being captured. Their captors had chopped off their heads so they would not grow up to be enemies. The tribes were always at war, the pilot-photographer had told him, and the Naga head hunters believed in decapitating all of the young men they found. Luckily, the pilot had his money belt and his supply of Indian coins, all dated before the start of the global hostilities, and was able to purchase his freedom.

The nurse with the impersonal voice told him he was leaving for the States.

"What time is it?" he said, asking the same inane

question he had asked so many times. "What's the date?"

"It's 0700," she said, and he knew before she spoke that she would call out the military time. "It's the 27th."

"Of what?" he said.

"Of January, captain," she said.

He had cracked up a month and four days ago. It could have been a year or two days. For him, time was meaningless, and he chided himself again for even asking about it.

When he was wheeled out of the ward, Joe Willoughby wished him luck. So did the orderly, Henry Daley, who had instructed him to control his dreams, and the doctors and nurses who had cared for him, although to him at Casablanca there had been only cold but efficient hands and disembodied voices. They had been too busy, thought Charley, excusing them, to be friendly.

Inside the C-54, similar to the plane which had carried him from Cairo, after he was strapped to the rack, he felt a hand on his arm.

"Hi, captain," said the warm voice of Marie DesChesne. "You're looking better."

"I thought you deserted me," he said.

"I told you I was going to the states with you."

"That's a relief. I need a lot of fluids, Marie."

"I know about that, captain. I've been given instructions to keep you full of fluids. The doctor was very explicit about that."

"What doctor?"

"Major Bart McDonough," she said. "He's quite concerned about you."

"Major McDonough? Is he one of the doctors in the hospital here?"

"Of course, captain. He was in charge of your case."

"Well, what do you know about that? I'll have to write him sometime and apologize. I thought nobody here cared about me."

"Everybody cares, captain. It's just that they've been so busy."

"That's what I figured."

The C-54 bore down the runway. He braced his mind for the inevitable thrust that would push the open wounds of his head into the pillow. He focused his thoughts on Miriam, and her voice became the nurse's voice. Miriam's face hung in his mind.

The pain came, but only for an instant. He pushed it away with the help of his wife in far-away Alabama. He slept.

Charley was driving a 1936 Ford. It was only three years old.

"How much did you pay for it?" said Daddy Woods.

"Only $150," said Charley.

"That's a nice looking car, all right, Charley. Where did you get the money? You're only 18 years old."

"Working in a restaurant last summer when we went back to Los Angeles. Don't you remember?"

"What did you do in the restaurant, Charley?"

"Baked biscuits."

"That's good work, Charley. A fellow can make good money baking biscuits."

"That's all right for a kid. I think it's better to own a restaurant."

"What in the world are you doing, Charley? That's ten biscuits you've eaten so far. Where are you putting it all?"

"I'm just hungry, that's all. Thinking of those biscuits made me want some."

"Are you all right, captain?" said Marie.

"I'm just hungry," he said. "Do you think you could feed me some of that baby food they're giving me?"

"Of course, captain. I bet you'll be happy when you get to bite into some solid foods again."

"I sure will. Say, Marie, who all's on this plane with us?"

"Mostly American soldiers going home. There's a Russian officer, too. I understand he was badly wounded at Stalingrad and he's going to an American hospital for treatment."

"Where they taking me, Marie?"

"I don't know, captain. I suspect they'll be sending you to a hospital in Alabama."

"Listen, Marie. You got to help me. Colonel Hull back in Calcutta said the best place for me is Valley Forge General Hospital in Pennsylvania. Don't let them send me anywhere else."

"You'll be close to your family in Alabama, captain."

"I know, but Colonel Hull said they could do more for me at Valley Forge. You got to help me."

"I'll do my best, captain."

The plane stopped for refueling at Reykjavik in Iceland and Gander in Newfoundland. Charley was taken to the infirmary at both places for medication and new wrappings. They landed at night at McGuire Air Force Base in New Jersey.

"Well, captain, we're here. Good old U.S.A."

"Don't forget, Marie," he said, mustering all the urgency he could dredge up. "Valley Forge General Hospital."

"I'll do my best, captain. That's a promise."

Charley felt Marie's hand on his arm after he had been

65

lifted out of the plane and to the ground.

"I've got to go now, captain," she said. "They're going to take you to the dispensary to clean you up. I'll tell them what you said about Valley Forge. Good-by, captain. Good luck."

"Good-by, Marie," he said, feeling a lump come to his throat. "God bless you. I'll never forget you."

She was gone now, and he wondered, as he was being hurried off in the cold, winter wind, which was a relief to him after so many hot days, what she looked like. As it was, he carried in his brain an angel's face.

"Valley Forge General Hospital," he said, as the new dressings were being placed on him. "Valley Forge General Hospital."

"What did you say, captain?" said a doctor or an attendant.

"Valley Forge General Hospital. That's where I'm supposed to go from here."

Still murmuring "Valley Forge General Hospital," fighting the weariness luring him to sleep, Charley was wheeled out of the building and rolled into an ambulance.

An attendant rode in the back with him.

"Where we going?" said Charley.

"Some place in Pennsylvania, captain. I think they said Valley Forge."

Charley let go then and went to sleep.

CHAPTER TEN

"I don't know how this guy made it, Andy. It's a wonder he's still alive after getting burned like this, and it's a wonder he's still alive after the beating he took getting here."

Charley, returning to consciousness, perceived the light showing through the layers of vasoline, but he lay still. Now, he thought, if he didn't reveal his awareness, he would hear a straight, unvarnished account of his condition.

"You're right, Major Cannon. He could have given up a long time ago. He must want to live awful bad. He's almost completely dehydrated. He's lost a lot of blood. His chemical balance is way off. He was almost dead when they brought him in."

Charley realized that he had been shorn of his dressings and that he was lying on something higher than a bed, probably a table. The stomach of one of the speakers occasionally brushed against his arm, and the voices were directly over him. To the side of his head, he heard the rustle of a starched nurse's uniform. The rustle moved away. He felt the needle in his arm and figured he was being given a transfusion.

"It's a tough one, all right, Andy. Our first job is to keep him alive. If we do that, then we've got to do a complete rebuilding job on his face. He needs a new nose, new lips and new eyelids. We've got to reconstruct his cheeks and graft his head. There's not enough good skin left on him for the grafting work that has to be done."

"You're right. The fire destroyed his dermal barrier. He's losing all his fluid through the burned areas. Until we can get some skin to grow on the damaged parts, particularly his hands, the only way we can keep some kind of fluid balance is by pouring it in him and hope that he doesn't lose it all."

"Nurse, let's cover him up now."

Charley's face, neck, head and hands were wrapped. He moved his arm, indicating that he was awake.

"He's coming around now, Doctor Moore," said the nurse.

"Hello, captain. Can you hear me?"

"Yes, sir," said Charley.

"This is Doctor Moore. Andy Moore. How do you feel?"

"A little weak, doctor."

"You've had a tough time of it, captain. You took quite a beating on those plane rides. Well, you won't be traveling for a while. We're going to make sure you're comfortable."

"Thanks, doctor."

"I'll come by to see you in the morning after you've had a good rest. Good night."

"Good night, sir."

Charley was only fuzzily aware of what was happening to him. He slid in and out of unconsciousness. His arms were constantly attached to needles. Bandages were always coming on and going off. His only sustenance now came through the needles stuck in his veins. When he was conscious, only for a few minutes at a time, he felt his body being scraped, and dimly realized that the dead skin was being removed.

"My God," he heard a nurse say, "I bet he doesn't weigh 80 pounds. He's nothing but bones."

There were no restraints on the comments of those attending him, since he was more dead than alive, and certainly unhearing, they thought, and many times he heard someone wonder what was keeping him alive.

"Charles?" said a voice, questioningly. "Charles?"

Teetering always on the edge of unconsciousness, Charley came awake.

"Miriam," he said, murmuring through the mask. "Is that you, Miriam?"

He listened for her voice and heard only the noise of running feet.

"She'll be right back, captain," said the nurse, Louise Cummings.

Tense now, fully awake for the first time in weeks, Charley listened for Miriam's return. He strained to hear the opening of the door. The door opened and there was somebody beside him, a hand touching his leg.

"Hello, Charles," said Miriam. "It's good to see you again, honey."

"I'll be all right now, Miriam," he said. "Now that you're here I'll be all right."

"They're going to let me stay here for awhile, Charles," she said. "I'll be able to see you everyday."

"How's Freddie," he asked.

"Just fine, Charles. Just fine. He's been walking for four months now, since he was 10 months old."

"Let's see," said Charley, counting fingers in his head. "He was born in December. Is it February already?"

"That's right, honey. It's February 4th."

"How long have you been here?" he asked, finding it difficult to speak, slurring his words as he was being pressed back into the dark world which had become his home.

"Two days, honey," she said, hurrying her soft speech, realizing he was drifting away. "Mrs. Atkinson called and told us. Her husband's right across the hall. She saw you come in and heard you were from Dothan. She lives just down the road in Columbia."

Charley nodded and left them.

His periods of consciousness lasted longer now, now that he knew Miriam would be there to talk to him. More and more, when she was there, he fought to stay awake.

"Where you staying, Miriam?" he asked on one of her visits.

"I thought I told you, honey. They gave me a room here so I could be near you."

He didn't know that these facilities were made available only to the families of patients expected to die.

"Is Freddie all right?" he asked.

"Yes, honey. I call home every day. They say he's growing like a horse."

It was Halloween Day and they were living in Los Angeles.

"Where you going, Charley?" said Daddy Woods.

"Out to play trick or treat," said Charley.

"Don't you remember that I told you that you couldn't go out tonight, Charley?"

"Come on, daddy. Halloween only comes once a year."

"You should have thought about that, Charley, when you acted up in school," scolded Daddy Woods. "I told you the next time you acted up you were going to be punished and I meant it. I guess you just didn't believe me."

"Golly, dad, all the other kids are out playing. What am I going to do all alone?"

"Well, you can play with me. What do you want to play?"

"Cowboys and Indians," said Charley. "I'll be the Indian and you'll be the cowboy. I'll capture you and tie you up."

"Okay, Charley," said Daddy Woods, smiling. "Come on and catch me and tie me up."

Charley grasped his father around the legs and pushed him unresistingly in a chair.

"All right, daddy, you're captured. You're supposed to sit there until I get a rope and tie you up."

Charley raced to the kitchen and found a clothes-line. He tied Daddy Woods to the chair.

"Now you're supposed to get loose and chase me," said Charley.

Daddy Woods strained against the rope.

"You really got me hogtied, Charley," he said.

Charley ran out the door and played trick or treat. When he returned, at midnight, he found his father sitting at the kitchen table. Charley feared the worst. Daddy Woods looked at him and began laughing.

"Charley," he said, "That's the last time I'm going to play the cowboy. It took me an hour to get loose."

He couldn't understand how he got there from California, but Charley was standing in front of the orphanage. His brother, Jack, came out the door. He thought it strange that Jack was wearing a man's suit but still had his little boy's face.

"Hey, Charley," he said, "I was just in there asking

about you. I wanted to know where you went. They wouldn't tell me."

"I was just in there myself, Jack, asking about you. They wouldn't tell me anything, either. Where you been, Jack?"

"Oh, I've been around, Charley. Where you been?"

"I'm in the Air Corps, Jack. Can't you tell from my uniform?"

"Hey, that's right. It's funny I never noticed it."

"I've been looking everywhere for you, Jack. Everywhere I go I ask about you."

"Same here, Charley. Well, I'll be seeing you."

Jack walked backwards into the orphanage, waving at Charley just as he entered the door. That's another strange thing, thought Charley. The door opened by itself.

"Wait, Jack," yelled Charley, running after him. "Wait."

He rushed into the orphanage and found himself standing in a field. He thought it remarkable that a door should open onto a field. Jack was gone.

Charley woke up in the closet. He remembered crying himself to sleep. It was against the rules for the children to play on the roof without permission. He had opened the door with a safety pin. The other kids followed him.

"Charles," said Miss Wilson, "don't you know you could have fallen off that roof and broken your neck? Don't you know you're not allowed up there unless there's somebody there to watch you?"

Miss Wilson put him in the closet and locked the door. He screamed and cried but nobody would let him out.

"How do you feel, Charles?" said Miriam.

"Please let me out," he said. "I won't do it again."

"Charles, this is Miriam. Are you all right?"

He realized that the closet was the mask that covered his eyes.

"Where you been, Miriam?" he murmured. "You've been away a long time."

"I've been here, Charles," she said, and he heard her sobs.

"What's the matter, honey?" he said.

"Hello, Charley," said a man's voice. "This is Dr. Moore. Glad to have you back with us. How you feeling?"

"A little weak, doctor," he said. "What happened?"

"You've been out for three weeks, Charley. We've had a devil of a time trying to keep you with us. All right, Mrs. Woods, he's all right now. It's time you went and got some sleep."

"I'll see you later, hon," said Miriam. She put her hands on his shoulder and he felt the soft touch of her face on his arm, the barest whisper of a touch, one that did not hurt him.

"You had everybody worried, son," said Dr. Moore after Miriam left the room.

"I felt like I'd been on a trip somewhere," said Charley. How are my chances?"

"Son, there was some fluid in your lungs and you passed out on us. You didn't have much chance then. If everybody had your will to live we wouldn't lose anybody."

"I've got to get back to Alabama," he said. "I'm going to make it."

"That's the spirit, captain," said Dr. Moore. "Keep thinking that way and you'll be out of here in no time at all."

"Is my wife still staying at the hospital?"

"That's what I understand. She's been to see you every day. That's a fine girl you've got there, son."

"I didn't think she was here."

"She was, but for three weeks you didn't know it."

Time didn't mean anything to him still, and he didn't know how long it was after he had returned to consciousness that he was rushed to the emergency room. All he knew was that he was on an operating table.

"Son," said Dr. Moore, "this is going to hurt. You're not strong enough to take a general anesthesia. We're going to put skin on those burned places. We'll do our best not to hurt you too much. Try to think of something else."

Nurses and attendants held him while Dr. Moore and his colleagues planted skin on his body. Sometimes the pain grew almost too much to take. Charley tried to faint but couldn't. He dozed off, but sleep always vanished with the sharp cut of a surgical knife. Finally, the pain left and sleep came.

Three hours later, when he woke in his room, Miriam was sitting beside him. Her presence lifted him up, and he believed he finally had made it across to the safe side of the river. He felt a return of strength.

"You all right, Charles?"

"I made it, Miriam. I made it."

"Yes, honey. I know. You're going to be fine."

Charley knew he was alive, but he also knew that he was still sick, but not sick as he had been. Now, he spent more time awake than asleep. His body no longer required long periods of unconsciousness.

Dr. Moore visited him several times a day.

"Say, doctor," said Charley one afternoon. "Why am I beginning to feel better. What happened in the operation room?"

"Well, Charley, you know that you were burned rather severely. The burns in most places were so deep that the dermal barrier was destroyed. Without this protection, your body could not retain the fluids you needed to live. We put skin on those burned places so that your body would retain the fluids."

"Was it my skin, doctor? I mean, I thought I had no skin that could be taken off me."

"No, son. It wasn't your skin. It came from a young man who worked in one of the wards. He died early that morning. His family gave us permission to use his skin. They said they would like to think that their son had helped save somebody's life."

"What did you do, doctor, call them up and ask them?"

"No, Charley. The boy was from Philadelphia. That's only 20 miles from here. I drove over and talked to the parents. They signed the papers we needed in order to use his skin."

"Thanks, doctor. Some day I want to thank them, too."

"There's time for that. Right now we've got to concentrate on building up your strength so we can start operating. We've only won half the battle. There's a lot of repair work we've got to do as soon as you're well enough."

"I'll be ready when you are," said Charley. "Say, doctor, is there any way I can get that needle out of my arm? It stays there most of the day sometimes."

"That needle is carrying fluids into your body. You're still losing water. That new skin hasn't taken hold yet. You need 5,000 CC's of fluids a day."

"How much is that, doctor?"

"About five quarts."

"Well, I'll drink five quarts a day. It'll be better than having that needle in me all the time."

"Are you sure you can drink that much, Charley?"

asked the doctor. "Five quarts, that's a lot of fluid."

"I'll have to do it, sir."

"Okay, let's give it a try."

Charley drank two or three glasses of water with each of his spoon-fed meals. His wounds had become massively infected, and he was given a penicillin shot every three hours. Each time, he drank at least two glasses of water. When he woke up during the night, between penicillin shots, he asked the nurse for water.

"Where are you putting all that stuff?" asked Dr. Moore.

"Well, sir, I'm not keeping it," Charley said.

The taste of water began to sicken him, and he asked for orange juice. He leveled out at nine quarts of juice a day.

The dead boy's skin died in six weeks, but it lasted long enough to enable Charley's body to achieve chemical stability. It had restored the skin barrier so that Charley could retain most of the fluids he took in. It had given Charley's body the time it needed to grow new skin. Charley no longer had to drink nine quarts of fluid a day.

Lying there, gathering strength for the difficult days ahead, Charley understood that he had conquered death. He knew that he had willed himself to live, but he was happy now to know that he no longer had this power of life or death in his hands. There were many times when, like animals tired of living, he could have allowed himself to go. He was relieved that he no longer had to fight for life. He believed he had waged his desperate battle because it was God's plan, that there was something for him yet to do.

CHAPTER ELEVEN

"Say, doctor," said Charley, "when will you take this bandage off my eyes so I can see?"

"We've got to keep them covered for awhile, Charley," said Dr. Moore. "They were ulcerated when you arrived. In their hurry to get you back to the States, they undoubtedly neglected to keep them moist. They dried out. If your eyelids had been working, they would have done the job for you. As it was, there was nothing to keep them wet and clean."

"Does that mean I'm going to have to get new eyelids, doctor?"

"That's right, Charley. As soon as your eyes heal properly, we'll go to work on the eyelids. First, though, while we're waiting for that, we'll start work on other parts of your face."

"Is it going to take a long time, doctor?"

"Charley, I'm going to be honest with you. You showed us how tough you are by staying alive. I'm going to make things as comfortable for you as I can, but it's going to take a lot of work, on everybody's part, and there are going to be times it'll hurt so much you'll wish the hell we never started."

"When do we start, doctor?"

"Sometime this week, Charley. I want to talk to you about that. These operations are going to take a lot of time. You'll be on the operating table for as long as three and four hours. Of course, you'll be under anesthesia while you're on the table. You'll feel nothing then, but afterwards it's going to hurt like the very devil. You will be given drugs to ease the pain. I want you to think about the problem of narcotics. There's the possibility that you'll become addicted. I want you to fight that. I want you to put off asking for a shot as long as you can, until you can't stand the pain anymore. The more you fight it, the less you'll be needing it."

"Okay, doctor. I'll do my best."

"Another thing, Charley," continued Dr. Moore, "narcotics play funny tricks on people. Sometimes they mess up a fellow so that he stops liking women. You understand what I mean?"

Charley thought about Miriam. He had a lot of living to catch up on.

"Yes, doctor, I understand. I'll have to hurt bad before I ask for dope."

"Okay, Charley. That's good. Now let me explain what we're going to do. We're going to work on your nose first. Then your cheeks, lips and chin. We'll take skin from other parts of your body and graft it onto your face. You've got to be very careful not to break or jar the skin once we've got it grafted. There are little capillary buds in the skin. After they stick their necks out, the slightest movement could have a guillotine effect. It would chop the necks and close the blood supply. Without blood, the grafts would die."

"What about my nose, doctor?"

"We're going to have to build you one, Charley."

"Well," he said, trying to make light of it, "make me a

good one, please. The one I had was a little too short."

"We'll make you one like John Barrymore's, Charley. Any more questions?"

"Yes, doctor. How about my hands? Will I have any hands?"

"I said I was going to be honest with you, Charley," said Dr. Moore, after a slight pause. "Your hands were in bad shape when you arrived. It's going to take a lot of surgery to save your thumbs and perhaps one or two fingers on each hand. There's a good chance they can be saved. After that, though, there will be months and months before you'll be able to use them."

Charley remained silent and Dr. Moore stared at the man lying rigid in his bed, as though seeking to penetrate the white mask for a glimpse of his reactions.

"We did our best, Charley. When you fell out of that plane, you landed in the middle of that flaming gasoline on your head and hands. Luckily, your instincts were still working and you kept your eyes closed. The ulcers that came because of lack of moisture can be cleared up. Your flight suit and your boots gave the rest of your body good protection. The burns you suffered where there was covering are not serious. Anything you want to ask me, Charley?"

Charley did not answer, and Dr. Moore interrupted the long, hurtful quiet with a cough.

"Well, Charley, that's about it. Your weight's up to 100 pounds. That's only 40 pounds under your normal weight. You've come a long way since you tipped the scales at a magnificent 80 pounds. You're getting to be strong enough to take the ordeal of surgery. You're still not the healthiest specimen around, you know, but we can't put it off any longer. There'll be plenty of risks for you, but after what you've been through I don't think anything can stop you."

"You're right, doctor," said Charley, speaking in a strained voice." There's nothing going to stop me from going back to Alabama."

So intent were the two men in their efforts to diagnose each other's true feelings, each hoping he could see through the gauze and tape to read the expressions on the other's face, that they were unaware of the presence of Miriam, who had entered the room during the latter part of their conversation. It wasn't until she spoke that they realized she had overheard them.

"Charles is right, doctor," she said speaking as determinedly as her husband. "Nothing's going to keep him from going home to Alabama."

"Hey, honey," said Charley. "I didn't hear you come in."

"I know," she said. "I heard the doctor say they're ready to start working on your face, Charles. That's good news, honey. In a little while you'll be good as new."

"Maybe I won't look like much, Miriam. For one thing, I don't think I'll have any ears. How about that, doctor. Are you going to make me some new ears? Somewhere, probably in Calcutta, I heard somebody say they had burned off."

"Heck, honey," said Miriam. "You can hear, can't you? That's what ears are for, anyway. The rest is all decorations."

"You're right, Charley," said Dr. Moore. "I don't think we'll be able to make new ears for you. Like Miriam says, though, you can hear, can't you?"

"What about Miriam, doctor?" said Charley. "Don't you think she ought to go home to Alabama and wait until I can go back all fixed up?"

"Like fun," she broke in. "I'm going to stay right here,

and Freddie, too, until we can all go back together. I'm going to get an apartment in town for me and Freddie. I'm going to Alabama one day next week and get Freddie. We're going to stay right here."

"Mrs. Woods, why don't you just stay in the hospital here?" said Dr. Moore. "There's no reason why you should get an apartment in Phoenixville."

"Honest, doctor, I want to tell you the truth. The folks staying in the rooms here are just sitting around waiting for their husbands or sons to die. It's depressing. Charles is not going to die. Heck, we just got married when this thing started. I'm not aiming to be a young widow."

"That settles it, Charley, I guess," said Dr. Moore, putting one hand on Charley's shoulder and the other on Miriam's arm. "Mrs. Woods is going to stay in town."

"I guess so," said Charley. "I never knew I married such a stubborn woman. Just the same, I hate it that she's going to sit around here and watch me get fixed up a little at a time. I'd much rather she'd go home and wait for me to come home all in one piece."

CHAPTER TWELVE

It was on May 25, 1945, that the doctors began building Charley's face from the skin of his arms, legs, hips and stomach. He knew it was May 25 because he told Dr. Moore he was going to time the reconstruction from start to finish.

"I want to see how good you people are," he said. "I'm going to hold a watch on you. What's the date and time?"

It's May 25th, 7 in the morning," said Dr. Moore. "You're going to wear out a lot of watches before we're through, Charley."

Just before he surrendered to the ether, falling away into nothingness, he pondered the possibility of changing his birthday from September 30 to May 25. It wasn't his real birthday, anyway.

Charley and Jack were playing in the yard of the orphanage with the other kids.

"How old are you?" one boy asked Jack.

"I'm six," said Jack.

"When's your birthday?"

"The first of October," said Jack. "When's your's?"

"June 10," was the answer.

The other boys called out their birthdays.

"When's your birthday?" Charley was asked.

Charley wasn't about to tell them he didn't know. He could lie as well as Jack could.

"The last day of September," he said.

He came back from the operating room and discovered that his right arm was lashed to his head. There was an ache in the biceps area that had not been there before he went to surgery.

"What's happened to my arm?" he said, awkwardly turning his head to face Dr. Moore, who, as usual after an operation, sat beside the bed.

"We're using the skin of your arm to make a covering for your nose, Charley," he said. "We cut away the skin and put it on your face. The other end is still attached to your arm. That's so the skin will stay alive and keep growing. We've wrapped your arm to your head so that the skin will stay in place."

"How long will I have to hold my arm this way?"

"It could be two weeks or even three weeks," said the doctor. "We've got a splint on your arm to keep it straight. We couldn't take any chances. The slightest movement could kill the skin."

"I'm beginning to hurt bad, doctor."

"You've been through quite a lot today. Hold off as long as you can before asking for a shot, Charley. I've left instructions with the nurse to give you something as soon as you ask for it."

"I've been holding off asking for drugs. The only time I ask is when I can't stand it anymore."

"I know, Charley. I know. The nurses have been talking about that. I'm going to change the medication every few days. That's so you won't become dependent on any one kind."

"Thanks, doctor. How long is all this going to take?"

"It's going to take quite a while, Charley. Sometimes the graft won't take and we'll have to do it over."

"More than a year, doctor?"

"I believe so, Charley. There's a lot of work to do on you. We can't operate every day. We've got to give you time to rest between visits to the operating room."

While the skin of his arm was growing to form his nose, Charley went to surgery to have his cheeks and chin fashioned. Small pieces of skin were pressed and stitched to his face. At the end of 22 days, the flap of skin on his nose was sliced from his arm. It had taken root and was growing.

"Okay, Charley," said Dr. Moore. "We've won a big battle with that. After it heals, we'll be able to work on your nose to shape it."

"How long will that take, doctor?"

"About six months, Charley. It will require six or seven operations."

In August, Charley's eyes had been cleared of ulcers. The bandages were removed.

"Can you let me have a hand mirror?" he said. "I want to see what I look like."

"I don't have a hand mirror," said the nurse.

Charley waited until she left the room. He got out of bed and staggered to the bathroom. He went in and looked in a mirror. He saw the angry lump of nose, a misshapen mass of red putty. His eyes stared out of red circles rimmed with skin scarred in ragged lines. He saw the differing hues of skin where the small, grafted squares were growing together, the junctures forming dotted indentations. It was a face like none he had ever seen.

He went back to bed and fell promptly asleep. When he

awoke, it was morning, and it was a morning he could see, for the first time in eight months, with the sun coming through the window to show a triangle of light on the hardwood floor. It was the first time he had seen all of a morning, and not a piece of it, as when his bandages were changed, like an occasional face and a slice of ceiling. He marvelled at the magic of sight, not realizing until that moment how wonderful it was to see again. He went to the window. It was the ending of summer. He saw the wide, expansive grounds of the hospital stretching out to the green trees of a forest.

He touched the wood of the sill and put the bandaged ball of a hand on the glass. He turned and looked at his bed, and the two straight-backed chairs, and a dresser, where he saw a framed picture of Miriam and Freddie. He picked up the picture between his bandaged hands and was staring at his dear ones when he heard the door open.

It was the orderly with his breakfast.

"Good morning, captain. How you doing this morning?"

The orderly looked up and saw Charley staring at her.

"Hey, captain," she said, smiling, "they finally took the bandages off. That's great."

"So you're Jean Gazinski," he said. "I tried to imagine what you looked like from your voice."

"Well, do I pass?"

"You sure do, Jean. You go to the head of the class. You're prettier than I thought."

He stared into the brown eyes of the blonde girl. He took in the soft curves that an austere white uniform could not hide.

"Come on, captain," she said, smiling. "It's time to eat. Open up." She held a glass of orange juice to his mouth.

Between bites of the ham, potatoes and eggs that she fed him, Charley questioned her, unwilling to let her go.

"What's a girl like you doing taking care of guys like me?" he said.

"Somebody has to do it," she said. "To tell you the truth, captain, I love working here. I came from Buffalo looking for a job and wound up in a night club in Philly. I was making good money and the tips were fantastic, but what I was doing wasn't important enough to suit me."

She became serious, and there was a pause in the conversation.

"Hey," she said, putting her smile back on, "you ought to be eating instead of talking."

"You know," he said, retreating from a probe of her private life, "this food is wonderful. It's the first meal here I've enjoyed. I can see what I'm eating. You ought to try eating with your eyes closed sometimes. Everything tastes the same."

"I guess you're right, captain."

"Part of the joy of eating, Jean, is looking at the beauty of the food. Your eyes see the food and notify the brain. The brain yells down to the palate, 'Hey, down there, a juicy hunk of steak is on the way.' So you're ready for it. When you chomp into a piece of steak you know it's steak. See what I mean?"

"Here," said Jean, holding the fork to his mouth. "Here's a hunk of ham. Put your communications system to work. Tell them the ham's coming."

"What did you do at that night club in Philly, Jean?" said Charley, somewhat hesitantly, reopening a subject she had tried to close earlier.

"Oh, there was nothing wrong with the work," she said.

86

"I was a waitress, but the pay was wonderful, for a girl. And, as I said, you couldn't beat the tips. What got to me, though, was watching a lot of guys throwing money around while a lot of other guys were fighting a war. I heard they needed orderlies out here and I applied. I'm not making any money, but I'm doing something that makes me feel good."

"Did you say you came from Buffalo?" said Charley.

"Buffalo, New York, where they invented snow."

"Listen, Jean, you've never seen snow until you've flown the Hump."

"How was it, captain? I mean, I've read about all those planes going down over there."

"It was rough, Jean. Real rough. You had to fight your way all the time. If you relaxed for a minute, the winds at the top would blow you against the side of a mountain. If you flew too high, the ice formed on the wings and weighted you down. You'd have to drop to the warmer air to melt the ice and then go back up. You had to go back up because there were so many peaks at the lower levels that the odds against you getting through were practically zero. There are too many mountains to hit when you're flying low."

"Say, captain, soon as you're able to get around I want to take you to South Philadelphia and blow you to a real feed."

"South Philadelphia? Is that a part of Philadelphia?"

"Hey, captain, that's a good guess. You hit it right on the nose. South Philly is where all the good eating places are. They've got Italian restaurants there that sell their recipes to Rome. You never ate such food in your life. There's a place called Palumbo's. I want to take you there and show you what eating's all about."

"Okay, Jean. Thanks. Maybe I'll take you up on that."

Charley enjoyed Jean Gazinski's visits, relishing her tomboy manner. She acted as though there was nothing unusual about Charley's face. She laughed and joked with him as though he were as normal-looking as anybody else.

Later that month, Charley was taken again to the operating room.

"This is the day we give you some new eyelids, Charley," he heard Dr. Moore say, just before the ether marched in and took command of him.

He was sitting on a field watching a bonfire. He was wearing his shorts, and he wondered about that, particularly since Ralph Keele, who was seated beside him, was wearing his flight clothes.

"Hey, Charley, what did you want to tell me?"

"I'll be taking a trip, Ralph, and I wanted you to tell the new guys that they never should touch the brakes until the plane's in the air. If you hit the brakes too soon you'll run out of runway and never be able to lift it off the field. Understand, Ralph?"

"What do you mean you're taking a trip?"

"I'm awful homesick, Ralph. I'm going home to Alabama to see the wife and kid. I'll only be gone a couple of hours."

"Oh. Well, all right, Charley, I'll tell them about the brakes. Don't forget you've got fly the Hump tonight."

"I'll be back in plenty of time, Ralph. I'm taking a fighter plane. I don't want to be lugging 28,000 pounds of gasoline to Alabama and back."

"Have a nice trip, Charley. Give my best to Miriam and the baby."

He swung into the cockpit and a live coal struck his right eye. He screamed in agony. He saw the blurred face of a doctor leaning over him. The doctor was wearing a white cap and a gauze mask.

"Captain," the doctor was saying, "we're stitching up your right eye. The knife slipped. You've got to hold your head still. We haven't got time to put you under again. We're putting drops in your eye, but it will only help a little. You've got to keep your head still."

With the strength of his mind, Charley held his head in a vise. He lay perfectly still and screamed as the pain gathered in his brain, and then exploded. He brought the fighter plane down on a green field behind his house. Miriam and Freddie came running out the door.

"What are you doing home?" said Miriam, as he swung his wife and baby in a circle of joy. "I thought you were supposed to be in India."

"I just thought I'd fly over to see you for a few minutes," he said. "I was homesick. I'm going right back."

"How do you feel, Charley?" said Dr. Moore.

"What happened, doctor?" he said. His right eye still throbbed with pain, but someone had extracted the live coal.

"They were grafting on a eyelid, Charley, when the doctor's knife slipped. It cut your eye and they had to stitch it up right away. You were coming out of anesthesia while they were sewing you up. There was no time to put you under again. That was a remarkable thing you did, Charley, holding your head still while they worked on you."

"It was not pleasant."

"I know it wasn't, Charley. I know it was nothing but pure hell."

Charley had never known what was happening in the operating room. He was anesthetized before he entered and unconscious when he left. However, he had sensed the frenzied activity while his eye was being stitched. There were weights on his legs. He felt that his body was in a strait jacket and he knew that his arms were being held.

"Do they have to hold me down like that all the time, doctor?"

"No, Charley. They had to hold you down this time because you were conscious. They had to put two orderlies across your legs and they wrapped a sheet around your upper body. A couple of nurses held your arms so they wouldn't thrash around."

Charley had thought that only Dr. Moore was working on him, but the voice he heard in surgery was that of a stranger.

"Who was the doctor stitching me up?" he asked. "I thought you were my doctor."

"Charley," said Dr. Moore, "you don't know how many doctors you've got. You've got the best surgery team in the world putting you together."

"Who are they?"

"Well, the principal surgeon on the case is James Barrett Brown. The others who have worked on you are Bradford Cannon, Carl Lischer, Jim Jensen, and Joe Murray."

"Are they military or civilian?"

"They're in the Army now, like me. Brown and Cannon are colonels. The others are majors. They're all quite famous in the field of plastic surgery. They joined the Army because so many men were being disfigured in combat. They wanted to help put them back together again."

"What's your speciality, doctor? In civilian life, I mean?"

"I was in general practice, Charley. I did just about everything there was to do."

"How come they're all colonels and majors and you're a captain, like me?"

"Seniority, Charley," he said, laughing. "Most of the doctors came in as captains and were promoted up. It took me almost a year to find somebody to take my practice before I could enlist."

Charley looked forward to his talks with Dr. Moore, believing he was the one person in the hospital who would tell him the truth about his progress. Miriam came every day, sometimes spending all of the daylight hours in the chair beside his bed. Always bright and optimistic, she believed, he thought, that one day he would emerge from his cocoon of bandages as unblemished and unscarred as he used to be. She would always tell him how well he looked.

"Sugar," she'd say, "you look fine, just fine."

Jean Gazinski dropped in several times during the day to feed him a diet of soft soap.

"Hey, captian," she'd say, cheerfully, "you're doing great."

CHAPTER THIRTEEN

Charley was kneeling in the dirt. A Japanese soldier was adjusting Charley's head on a chopping block. He marvelled that the lump of wood so closely resembled the butcher blocks he had seen in the grocery stores back home. He thought he was dreaming and tried to force himself to waken. Still, the sun burned hot on his head and neck, and his bent-over back began to ache.

"Yankee," said the voice above him, and Charley lifted his head to look up at a Japanese officer. "I'm sorry we have to do this, Yankee, but you give us no choice."

"Where did you learn to speak English like that?" said Charley, having nothing else to say.

"I studied at Harvard," said the enemy, somewhat proudly. "It'll be over in a minute, captain. Actually, there'll be very little pain."

Charley, who had declined the use of a blindfold, saw his executioner behind the officer. He was a tall, broad man stripped to the waist. With big, strong hands he gripped the handle of a heavy sword. He swung the sword at the trunk of a small tree, and, for a moment before it toppled, the tree stayed in place. Would his head and body remain together for an instant like that, he wondered?

Charley tried desperately to speak to the Japanese officer.

"I think he's coming around," said a voice. It was Dr. Moore's. "He's coming out of it, Mrs. Woods."

He realized that he had been dreaming. He heard Dr. Moore addressing his wife.

"He's going to be all right. You ought to go home now and get sleep. Better still, why don't you spend the night in one of the guest rooms?"

"What happened, doctor?" said Miriam.

"We had to interrupt the operation, Mrs. Woods. As you know, he suffered very severe burns. Consequently, each graft requires major sugery. His heart's not strong enough yet for the amount of work that has to be done in each operation. He's out of danger now. Why don't you try to get some rest?"

"I'll just sit a few minutes more, doctor. Then I'll go home and take care of Freddie. The baby-sitter's been there all night and has to go home to get her own children off to school."

"All right, Mrs. Woods. Don't worry your head about Charley, now. He's going to be all right."

Charley, too, tried to speak to Miriam, to tell her he was going to be all right. He formed the words in his brain but could not find the strength to utter them. He managed to make a sound, though, and Miriam pressed her head to his.

"Charley?" she said. "Charley? What is it, hon?"

"Didn't I tell you he's going to be all right?" said Dr. Moore, and Charley detected the happy note in his voice.

Later, after Miriam had gone, he heard Dr. Moore speaking to one of the nurses.

"This boy's had a rough time of it tonight, nurse," he said. "I don't want you to leave him for a minute. I'm going down to the office and sack out on the couch. I think he's going to be okay, but if he starts to slip at all call me immediately. Understand? Immediately."

"Yes, doctor," she said.

Charley, lying there still, was aware that he hovered between life and death. He wasn't going to die, he told himself, and again he tried to speak in order to reassure the doctor. Failing that, he turned his mind back to the dream and wondered why he had dreamed of execution, of all things.

Fuzzily, and in out-of-focus snatches, he recalled a night he had been grounded by fog at a Chinese airfield. He went to sleep beneath a wing of his plane. He was awakened by the shouts of many voices. He jumped to his feet and ran to join a group of pilots standing at the edge of the runway. They pointed to a bonfire burning on a hill to the east. Suddenly, a bonfire broke out on a hill to the west, and almost simultaneously, there was a bonfire on a northern hill.

"Bombing raid," he shouted, almost in unison with the others, and he ran for an underground shelter.

Seconds later, he heard the ear-shattering blasts of tons of Japanese bombs. He heard the roaring of the flames ignited by exploding gasoline tanks. The raid was over in minutes. Charley emerged from the shelter. He saw the enveloping fire in dozens of stricken planes, and the jagged, newly-built craters revealed by the spreading light.

Several hours later, he recalled, when the first streaks of the sun announced the coming of dawn, Chinese soldiers rode out in American jeeps to search for the saboteurs. It often happened in China that disloyal Chinese, paid by the Japanese, built such fires around Allied bases to point them out to enemy bombers. And it often happened, also, that the poor peasants found near the sites of the bonfires would lose their heads to the executioners' swords. This illogical twist of the logical Chinese mind always amazed Charley. Didn't they understand that the guilty parties would have vanished before the troops arrived, and that only the innocent would remain--to be executed?

Pondering this puzzle, he went to sleep.

CHAPTER FOURTEEN

"Where am I?" he said, his left eye trying to focus on the overhead light.

"It's all right, Charley," said Dr. Moore. "You're back in your room. You're going to be all right."

"I thought I was dead," said Charley.

"Well, you were, technically, for a couple of minutes, Charley. Your heart stopped while they were planting skin on your neck and head. They gave you artificial respiration until the beat returned. Take it easy now. You're going to be fine."

"You sound like Miriam, now," Charley said.

"He's right, hon," said Miriam. "You're going to be just fine."

Before he drifted off again, he was conscious of the needle in his arm and saw, as if in a distance, the upside-down bottle on a stand near his head. He fuzzily wondered why they had started feeding him intravenously again.

His weight up once more, Charley returned to the operating room. Each time that his heart stopped, as it did twice more in the ensuing months, he dreamed his dream of death.

He stood beside a weeping Miriam in a small country

church. His brother, Jack, and P.A. Woods came up to offer their condolences. He shook their hands but could not understand the words they said with choked voices.

"Who's dead, honey?" he whispered in Miriam's ear.

"You are, dear," she replied, now sobbing out of control, and, then, she stared at him with startled eyes.

"Charley," she said, "what are you doing out of your coffin?"

He was flying the Hump in a snowstorm that tossed his plane from peak to peak. Ice formed on the wings and forced the B-24 down to the warmer air, close to the cluster of lower peaks, where hundreds of his friends had fallen, and the storm abated. The skies were clear and the sun was shining.

Directly below him, on a narrow, dirt road, he saw a black hearse and a Model T Ford proceeding slowly between the rows of oaks and pines that ranged haphazardly along the sides. Behind the two vehicles, from the place where they had come, Charley saw the stilted shack in which he had lived as a boy.

He brought the big plane down until it hovered just above the hearse. The roof was of glass, and Charley saw his name on a small brass plate. The Model T passed under the idled plane. Charley recognized it as the car that had taken him and Jack away from the orphanage. The car was being driven by P.A. Woods, and seated beside him was Aunt Annie Woods. In the back, he saw Miriam, Freddie and his brother. All wore black, and all were weeping except Jack. He was angry at Jack for not weeping. He'd tell him a thing or two the next time he saw him. He didn't see Grandma Woods. He leaned out of the Liberator.

"Where's Grandma?" he yelled.

The small procession stopped and Aunt Annie pushed over in the front seat to make room for Grandma Woods.

The cars turned into a cemetery. The wrought iron sign connected in an arc to white marble pillars said "Birmingham Cemetery." He took his plane to the burial plot and looked down as the coffin was being lowered in the grave.

"Stop," he called. "Stop. I'm not dead yet?"

"What did you say, Charles?" said Miriam. He knew the sounds of her voice well enough to recognize the tears. He had learned to read the meaning behind the words people said to him during the year his eyes had been imprisoned inside cloth and tape.

"What are you crying about, Miriam?" he said.

"Charles, I'm not crying. I was just wondering what you said."

"I said I wasn't dead, honey," he said.

"I know that, Charles. I was just a little worried, that's all."

"Where's Dr. Moore, honey?"

"I'm right here, Charley. Take it easy, boy. You had another rough morning in surgery. You're going to be all right."

He weakly turned his head to see Miriam and Dr. Moore, whose voices came from the left side of the bed, near the uncovered eye, and the effort proved to be too much for him. He fell asleep.

There was a strange face looking down on him when he awakened.

"Charley," said Dr. Moore, "this is the fellow making a new man out of you. Dr. James Barrett Brown."

"How you feeling, captain?" said Dr. Brown.

"I feel a little better, doctor," Charley replied.

"I'm still a little bit woozy right now, though."

"That's to be expected, son," he said. "You've been through a lot and you came thought with all flags flying."

"I got the idea sometimes I almost didn't make it," said Charley.

"We had to operate sometimes when you were quite weak, captain, but it had to be done. We had to make sure there was skin covering on some bad places, captain. They had to be covered so you wouldn't lose all your fluids. That was our biggest problem in your case. The burns were so deep there was nothing to keep the liquids inside. We managed to maintain a proper fluid level outside the operating room by pouring liquids into you, either by mouth or injection. Once in surgery, though, it was terribly difficult to get enough liquids in you to offset the loss that occurred during the operations."

"Am I over that part of it, doctor. I mean, do I have enough protection now to keep the fluids in?"

"Yes, son. The worst part is over, the part of keeping you alive. The transplanted skin is growing on all of the burned areas. What we've got to do now is wait for you to grow healthy enough so that we can start shaping the skin on your body. We've got to smooth out the rough places where the grafts are growing together. Dr. Moore tells me he has been frank with you throughout. I'll be just as candid. We've got a lot of work to do yet on your nose and hands. But you're out of the woods, captain. You're out of danger."

"Will I lose my right eye, doctor?"

"There's a chance we can save it, captain. It may have to be operated on again, also."

"What about my hands?"

"There was no skin on your hands, captain. It was

through your hands, incidentally, that you were losing much of your fluids. We had a more difficult time keeping skin there than anywhere else. There was very little flesh left on which to graft it. We virtually had to anchor it to the bones. Now we've got to wait until the skin grows flesh under it before we can begin corrective surgery on your hands. It may be another year, captain?"

"Another year? Heck, doctor, I've been here more than a year already. It looks like I'll be an old man before I get back to Alabama."

"Not quite, Charley," said Dr. Moore. "You're pretty much out of the woods now. As soon as you're strong enough, we're going to let you stay in town with Miriam and your son. You'll just have to come to the hospital when you're scheduled for an operation. After that, as your condition improves, you'll be able to go to Alabama between operations. You'll be away for 60 and 90 days at a time, depending on your progress."

"You're talking like I've got a long way to go, doctor. Right?"

"That's right, captain," said Dr. Brown. "When we finally discharge you from the hospital, we want to satisfy ourselves first that we did as much for you as we possibly could."

CHAPTER FIFTEEN

Once told he would be allowed to leave the hospital between operations, if his condition permitted, Charley began preparing himself for the great adventure in the world outside. He knew he was not entirely out of place at Valley Forge, where some of the worst victims of war had been assembled for the rebuilding of their faces and bodies. At the hospital, where unsightliness was not uncommon, there was nobody to disconcert him with embarrassed stares. It would be different, he knew, away from the protection and security of the hospital. He knew what he looked like. His bathroom mirror told him every day.

The stitched, red swollen flesh of his cheeks bulged out from between the dressings that still covered his nose, right eye, chin and head. His left eye peered out from beneath a thick, puffy lid that had been made from the skin of his arm. His mouth, also rebuilt from his arm, was a straight line that separated flaps of transplanted skin. There were no lips. The wrappings around his head, protecting the growing skin stripped from his stomach and hips, resembled a white turban.

With the help of Miriam he ventured out of his room to meet the world represented at Valley Forge, patients, doctors, nurses, attendants, visitors and office and work crews. He wanted to learn to react without inward flinching to the looks of awe and pity. He knew, too, that his appearance would serve to lift the spirits of parents and wives of patients disfigured or dismembered. This thought gave him courage. If he could help the morale of the mournful-faced civilians he saw in the corridors, why, then, he would be happy to patrol the hallways from sun-up to sundown.

His legs, uncertain and unsteady after 26 months of almost complete immobility, grew strong as he practiced to meet the world. Yet, he was not permitted to walk alone. His hands were still encased in balls of bandages resembling huge, white boxing gloves, to keep the bones from moving and breaking the new skin. If he stumbled and fell, the instinctive protective actions of his hands to break the fall would undo the arduous, painstaking months of plastic surgery. So Miriam was always with him.

Charley visited other patients on the floor, remembering with them adventures in a war that had long ago stopped, laughing at their escapes from danger, a stalled airplane, a jammed gun, an undetonated grenade, near misses that were funny only in retrospect. They even told, without emotion, of the actions that had brought them here, maimed and scarred. Mostly, they talked of war as though they had been spectators and not participants. To them, it was something that happened long ago and far, far away.

In the first week of his release from his room, Charley liked to visit the ward room at the end of the hall, where the ambulatory patients lived, and where there always was laughter and the warmth of camaraderie. It was the busiest place on the floor. Patients in wheelchairs, on crutches and in casts, everyone who could wheel, walk or hobble, were forever going into the ward to share in the fellowship.

On one visit, Charley saw a group of patients collected around a dignified old lady who sat in a corner of the room and read from a book of poetry.

"Who's that?" Miriam asked the ward attendant, who was standing near the door.

"She just came in and said she was from Philadelphia and said she was going to make the boys happy by reading poetry to them," he said.

"Is it any good?" said Charley.

"You see where I am, don't you?" said the orderly. "I was sneaking out when you came in."

As they talked, men on crutches and others in wheelchairs eased their way out of the ward. The circle around the poetess grew thinner, until, finally, she was left alone with a boy trapped in his bed by a tractioned leg. Charley and Miriam approached the pair. The eyes of the young man, about 18, Charley figured, shot them a plea for help. Charley caught the S.O.S.

"Can we do something for you?" he said.

"I hate to say this in front of ladies," said the youth, "but I need a bedpan bad. Could you get the orderly for me? Excuse me, ladies."

"I'll come back later," the old lady said.

The man in traction groaned.

"You'll feel better in a little while," she said, patting his hand.

Miriam called the orderly. He brought a bedpan and drew the curtain around the patient's bed.

Charley, Miriam and the old lady had moved toward the door.

"Ma'am," said Charley, "I understand you're from

Philadelphia. Is that right?" Charley was getting an idea.

"Yes," she said. "I live on Rittenhouse Square. I came over to read my poetry to you boys. I believe we all should do our part to make things better for our servicemen."

"I was thinking," said Charley, "that with all the boys there are in the Naval Hospital in Philly, you could do just as much without traveling so far. You could read to the boys there."

"I really admire the way you boys all think of each other," she said, tears coming to her eyes. "The boys at the Naval Hospital said the same thing about you. They said you were more deserving than they. Wasn't that nice?"

"Yes, ma'am," said Charley. "It sure was."

The old lady arrived promptly at 11 every morning and read her poetry until it was time to catch the 3 o'clock train. When the ward was empty, as it invariably was when word of her coming arrived in time, except for patients in traction, who had curtains drawn around their beds, she visited the patients in private rooms and read to them.

She stopped coming after her sixth day, and Charley and Miriam wondered why until they visited the ward. It was crowded again. Jokes were yelled from bed to bed. Patients played poker on card tables in corners of the room, hiding their money from the nurses. The room once more was filled with happy noises.

"What happened to the poetry lady?" Charley asked the attendant.

"I don't know, sir," he said, laughing, walking away.

Jean walked by carrying a tray.

"Hey, Jean," called Charley. "Come here, will you?"

"What's the story, captain?" said Jean. "What can I do for you?"

"Where's the poetry lady, Jean? I haven't seen her around lately."

"All right, captain, but don't give me away. She got a letter from somebody at the Naval Hospital in Philly telling her how much he missed her poetry. It was a real sad letter, captain. It'd make you want to cry."

"How do you know that, Jean?"

"I read it, captain. There's a newspaper guy in the ward. He wrote the letter and he gave it to one of the orderlies to mail from Philly. He gave him ten bucks to do it."

Charley never knew whether the swab jockeys in Philadelphia responded in kind, because he left the hospital shortly afterwards to take up residence in Phoenixville, in the apartment in which Miriam and Freddie had lived for two years. It was March of 1947, and the cold Pennsylvania wind, colder and sharper than any wind he remembered, was a fresh, invigorating change from the warm, antiseptic smell of the hospital. He breathed in the chilled air, through his hand-made mouth and nose, and exhilarated by the thought that he was free again. There was snow on the ground, Miriam helped him over an icy clump between the curbing and the car.

"Where to?" said Miriam.

"Home," said Charley.

CHAPTER SIXTEEN

With his arm wrapped around Miriam, Charley stared out the window of the car and delighted in the sights of the open, rolling countryside, the profusion of trees and bushes, now bare of leaves, and the neat, little houses with their broad lawns flaked with snow.

In the distance, Charley saw a tall chimney belching smoke.

"What kind of place is that, where that smoke's coming from?" he asked.

"That's a steel mill," said Miriam.

"Say," he told Miriam, "that reminds me of something. I get the impression now that while I was in real bad shape there was somebody praying for me. It's coming back now. I think I vaguely remember somebody saying that this girl used to come to the hospital every day to pray for me. The reason I just thought of it, I got the idea somehow that her daddy owns that steel mill."

"That's right, hon," said Miriam. "There was a girl who prayed for you every day. That's when we thought we were going to lose you. She was a pretty little thing. You're right about her daddy. One of the nurses told me who she was."

"Well, honey," said Charley, "I think one of the first

things we ought to do is call her up and tell her her prayers have been answered."

"My prayers, too, Charley," said Miriam, snuggling closer.

The car stopped in front of a square, white house on a quiet street.

"We're home, honey," said Miriam.

"There's a little ice here, captain," said a neighbor, putting his hand under Charley's arm. "You'd better let me help you."

"Thanks," said Charley, realizing he did not resent this first offer of aid from a stranger. After all, there was ice on the sidewalk.

As he stood on the walk, waiting for Miriam, Charley saw that a group of small children carrying books, apparently on their way home from school, had stopped near the car and were staring at him. He understood their curiosity. How often does one see a man in uniform with most of his face swathed in bandages, the dressing on his head showing below the rim of his officer's cap and big boxing gloves protruding from the slit ends of his sleeves?

A little girl approached.

"Hi, mister," she said.

"Hello, honey," said Charley. "You just get home from school?"

"Yes," she said, and she ran to join her group.

Miriam held on to his arm as they walked up the steps.

"Honey," he said, as she turned the knob of the door, "I'm worried about Freddie."

She had started to open the door. Now she pulled it shut.

"He just has to get used to you, Charles," she said.

"The last time I saw him he was just a baby," said Charley. "He doesn't even know who I am. He expects his father to look like other men. Maybe he'll faint like you did."

Miriam laughed and playfully nudged him with her shoulder.

"I haven't fainted since, have I?" she said. "Freddie knows his daddy's coming home today. So let's go in and show him what I've got."

A middle-aged woman, gray-haired and stout, was holding the three-year-old Freddie in her arms on a sofa. She rose with the child when Miriam and Charles entered.

"He's getting sleepy, Mrs. Woods," she said, staring at Charley and handing Freddie to Miriam. Charley saw her eyes widen with shock.

"This is my husband, Charles, Mrs. Wambach," said Miriam. "Charles, this is Mrs. Wambach. She's been spending more time with Freddie than I have."

"It's a pleasure to meet you, ma'am," said Charley warmly, pretending he had not seen the startled reaction to his quilted face.

"Nice to meet you, too, captain," she said, hurriedly, reaching for a coat on a chair and throwing it over her shoulders. "I've got to run now." And run she did, jerking the door open and racing from the house.

"I hope that doesn't happen every time I meet somebody," said Charley, jokingly. "The poor woman was scared half to death. I bet she's still running."

"I'm proud of you, Charles," said Miriam, showing her pride in him in a smile that lighted her face, and a tenderness that misted her eyes. "I'll never be afraid of how you handle people again."

Freddie, meantime, curled in his mother's arms, had come fully awake at the sight of the big man with the strange face and covered hands. His eyes, wide-open now, stared at Charley with curiosity. As Charley approached him, holding out the clubs of his hands, the expression changed to fear. He turned his face and burrowed his head in Miriam's shoulder.

"This is your daddy, honey," said Miriam, whispering in his ear. "Don't you want to show him how happy you are to see him?"

Freddie shook his head and tightened his hold on Miriam's neck, pulling her head down to his.

Charley walked behind Miriam and looked down at the hidden face of his son. Freddie promptly clamped his eyes shut.

"That's all right, son," said Charley. "You were no raving beauty the first time I saw you, either."

"That was some night," said Miriam, patting Freddie on the back, while Freddie turned to take a furtive look at his mother's friend.

Charley thought back to that frantic December night in 1943. He was stationed in Dallas, after his transfer to the U.S. Air Corps from the R.A.F., and was ferrying big planes to bases all over the country. He had orders to report to Love Field at 4 o'clock in the morning for another secret ferrying assignment. He had just returned from a flight to New York, only five hours before Miriam woke him.

"Oh," said Charley, scratching himself awake, "is it time for me to go again?"

"No, honey," she said, trying to sound brave. "It's time for me to go."

"What?" said Charley, uncomprehending.

"The baby's telling me it wants to be born," she said,

and then pain creased her face and she clapsed her stomach with both hands.

Charley looked at his watch. It was 3 o'clock. he was due at the field in an hour, which was 50 minutes away by car. Orders were orders, but he could ignore them, perhaps, this one time. But there was a war on, and there were no excuses for disobedience during war time. He could take Miriam to the hospital or he could obey his orders. He telephoned Miriam's closest friend, Sally Weiss. She lived a block away. There was no answer. There must be something wrong with her phone. He drove over and pounded on the door of her apartment. As he was standing there, desperately knocking the door down, Sally called out.

"Who is it?" she said. "What do you want?"

"It's Charley," he said. "Open the door. Miriam's ready."

As she opened the door to admit him, her husband, a night worker in a defense plant, arrived and entered the apartment with him. Charley knew from his expression that he suspected the worst.

"I'll explain later," Sally told her astonished husband as she followed Charley, running.

"You drive her to the hospital," said Charley. "I've got to get to the air field. I'll call a cab.'

When he returned to Dallas two days later, Charley found a tired but happy Miriam and a wrinkled, prune-faced baby in her hospital room.

There were only a few weeks for him to spend with the new baby before his request for overseas duty was approved, and Charley went off to India. An infant is not an elephant, thought Charley, standing in that Phoenixville apartment, and Freddie didn't know him from the man in the moon.

110

In the months that followed, between regular weekly visits to the hospital for minor repairs, before new major surgery was to be performed on his nose and hands again, Charley won his way into the little tyrant's heart. Miriam purchased a bigger automobile and the three of them visited the little farm communities around Phoenixville and occasionally, when the weather was bright, they motored over to Philadelphia. When they stopped for a bite to eat, or to read a roadside marker commemorating a battle of the Revloutionary War, the people they met stared at Charley's face, but Charley saved the embarrassed moment by speaking to the starers.

"How y'all doing?" he'd say in his open Alabama way, pushing through a wide-eyed, open-mouthed group.

"Fine, fine," they'd answer, speaking too loud, to cover their discomposure.

The apartment grew too small for them, particularly since Charley and Freddie liked to roll around on the floor, while Miriam worried about his face and hands, and Charley decided that they needed more room to live in. He had become reconciled to a longer stay, with his hands still resisting treatment, and the three of them went out one day and bought a house just on the edge of Phoenixville, only a mile from the hospital grounds. Charley still held on to his dream of Alabama, though, and Miriam, too, and the new house was just a way station.

They were wrestling in the living room one day, Charley and Freddie, and Freddie's foot accidently struck Charley's bandaged right eye.

The kick had sent a skyrocket shooting through his brain, but Charley hid the pain from Freddie. He pushed himself to his knees with his elbows and got to his feet.

"That's enough for now, Freddie," he said, keeping the agony out of his voice. "Your old man's tired."

"Are you all right, honey?" said Miriam, from whom he could hide nothing.

"Just a headache, honey. It'll go away."

Just before dawn he woke Miriam.

"Miriam, you'd better call Dr. Moore. There's something wrong with my right eye."

CHAPTER SEVENTEEN

When Charley and Miriam arrived at the emergency room, Dr. Moore was waiting for them, already attired in white coat. Charley saw that he was unshaven and his hair was tousled.

"I hated to wake you up, doctor," he said.

"You should have done it sooner, Charley, as soon as it happened."

"I thought it could wait until morning."

"Charley, the shape you're in, nothing can wait until morning. Well, you're here now. That's the important thing. Sit down here, Charley."

Charley sat in a straight-backed chair.

"Lean back a little, Charley," said the doctor, as he removed the dressing and swabbed the wounded eye with a solution out of a pan which the nurse had brought to him.

"I called Dr. Brown right after you called me," he said. "He'll be here any minute."

Even as he spoke, Dr. Brown entered the room. Charley heard the steps and then the doctor's soft voice.

"How does it look?" he asked.

"It's badly infected, Jim," said Dr. Moore.

Leaning back in the chair, stinging from the eye wash,

Charley waited for the fateful pronouncement. He had no illusions. His right eye had been undergoing treatment for more than a year, since it was accidentally cut on the operating table. He was constantly aware of the possibility that he might lose its sight. He prepared himself for the diagnosis that would mean the chipping away of another part of his body. What the heck, he told himself, he would still have his left eye. He had been getting along with just one eye for a long time. He thought of Tom Atkinson, his soldier friend across the hall. Tom had lost both eyes. He couldn't see at all. And he had lost both arms. Yet, nobody ever heard Tom complaining.

He heard the doctors conferring in quiet voices.

"There's no doubt about it, Andy," said Dr. Brown. "It's badly infected. We've got to take care of it right away."

Charley felt Miriam's fingers gripping into his left arm.

"That's what I figured, Jim," said Dr. Moore. "That's why I thought it was important enough to get you out of bed. Well, I'd better start making preparations. Examination's over, Charley. You can straighten out your head now."

"What's the verdict?" asked Charley.

"Your eye's in bad shape, Charley," said Dr. Moore. "It's infected and we're afraid the infection will spread if something's not done immediatley."

"You mean operate?" said Charley.

"That's right, Charley. I don't know if we can save it or not. Frankly, there's a strong likelihood that we'll have to take it out."

"You're the doctor, doctor," said Charley. "When you going to do it?"

"Right now, Charley. As soon as the room is ready. We were always afraid you might lose it, after that accidental cut when the scalpel slipped on the operating table."

A nurse opened the door.

"We're ready, Dr. Moore," she said.

The anesthetist placed something over Charley's face and mouth.

"Breathe deeply, captain," he said.

He heard the sounds of morning as he opened his eyes. Jack was sitting on the side of his cot, across the aisle from Charley's. He was crying.

"What's the matter, Jack?" he said.

"Don't you remember what happened yesterday?" Jack said.

"I don't remember," said Charley. "What happened yesterday?"

"Don't you remember they took us downstairs and let some more people look at us?" said Jack.

"That's right. I remember that."

"Remember how we said we'd always stay together? Well, they went and took Ross."

"Who's Ross?" said Charley. "Do I know Ross?"

"What's the matter with you, Charley? Ross is your own brother."

Charley tried as hard as he could to think if he knew somebody named Ross.

"Are you sure, Jack? I thought it was just you and me."

"Just the same, I remember him, even if you don't. I'm going out to find him."

"Let me go with you, Jack. I'll help you look."

But Jack was gone.

He heard Dr. Moore's voice.

"I think we got it in time. If we'd waited any longer the infection would certainly have spread to the point that he probably would have lost both of his eyes."

Which was the dream, thought Charley?"

"Hello," he said.

"Hi, honey," said Miriam. "Are you all right? You feel all right?"

"You'll be okay, Charley," said Dr. Moore.

"You didn't have to remove it?"

"That's right, Charley. We're going to wait and see how you do. We might be able to save it."

"Thanks, doctor. I know you'll do what you have to do. I guess I'll have to stay in the hospital awhile more now. How long will it be before I can go home?"

"We'll have to keep you for a week or so, Charley. We want to make sure the wound heals properly. Well, I'll be going. I'll look in on you later. Good-by, Mrs. Woods."

"Good-by, doctor, and thanks," said Miriam.

"Say, Miriam," said Charley, after Dr. Moore had left, "you remember me telling you about my brother, don't you?"

"Jack? Of course, silly. I even hunted for him when you were overseas. Nobody knows anything about him. The orphanage wouldn't tell me who adopted him."

"Well, I think I've got another brother. His name's Ross. I just had a funny dream about him, and I have a vague recollection that the dream actually happened. In the dream Jack was crying because some people came and took Ross away from the orphanage. Jack told me about Ross, and the more I think about it the more I seem to remember there were three of us. How do you explain all these dreams I'm having about Jack? It's like he's reaching out for me."

"It's more like you're reaching out for him, instead of Jack reaching out for you, Charles," she said, patting his arm.

116

"Did you ever think of that? How does your eye feel now?"

"Thinking about Jack and the idea that I have another brother made me forget all about my eye. It hurts some, but I can stand it. When we get back to Alabama, honey, we'll start hunting for Jack all over again. We'll look for Ross, too. I got a feeling that if we find one, we'll find the other."

He lay back and was silent.

"Tired, hon?" said Miriam.

"Yes, I am," he said. "All of a sudden, I'm awful sleepy."

"Go to sleep, then, Charles. I'll just sit here a while."

Jack had wiped away the tears and was standing over him.

"Tell me more about Ross, Jack," said Charley. "I'm trying as hard as I can but I don't remember much about him. I thought it was just you and me. I remember somebody came and got us. I was sitting in the front and you were in the back. I even remember the man asking us how old we were, but I don't remember anybody else. Where was Ross sitting?"

"He was in the back seat with me. I was holding him. He didn't want to go. Remember we went downstairs yesterday afternoon so some people could look at us and maybe adopt us? Don't you remember a man and a lady talking to Ross?"

"I remember going downstairs, all right," said Charley, "but I didn't even look at those people. I didn't want anybody taking me."

"Just the same, they took Ross. I asked Miss Wilson where he was going. She said they were just taking him out for a ride. He never came back, though."

Charley saw that Jack's bed had not been slept in. He

117

noticed for the first time that Jack was fully dressed and that his Sunday shoes were caked with dirt.

"You been out all night," Charley said, accusingly. "Miss Wilson will skin you alive."

"I've been looking for Ross. I walked all the way to Birmingham and back. I snuck out after everybody went to sleep. I just came back to tell you that I'm going to keep hunting for Ross until I find him. You wait here for us. Don't go and get adopted while I'm gone. Momma told me to take care of you."

"All right, Jack, I'll wait. I won't let anybody adopt me.
He heard Dr. Moore speaking.

"Charley's tough, Mrs. Woods, as tough a man as I've ever known. However, he has just suffered another setback. We're concerned about his mental attitude once he becomes fully aware of the possibility that he might lose his eye. We're hopeful we'll be able to save it. The only thing that has kept him fighting so long has been that dream of his to go back to Alabama. He could have quit a dozen time. Frankly, he has surprised a great many people here by staying alive. The danger now is that he might decide there's no point in fighting anymore. He might just up and quit."

"Charles will never quit," said Miriam. "For one thing, I won't let him."

"That's the girl," said Dr. Moore.

"Hello," said Charley, trying to break out of the dream, either the dream of Jack and somebody named Ross or the dream of Dr. Moore and Miriam. As he called, he wondered who would answer.

"Hi, honey," said Miriam. "It's about time you woke up. You going to sleep your life away?"

"How do you feel, Charley?" said Dr. Moore.

"Okay, I guess," he replied. "Well, when do I get out of here? I can't spend my life hanging around a hospital."

Miriam gave a little laugh, a happy laugh, and Charley detected the relief in her.

"About a week, Charley," said Dr. Moore. "We've got to keep tabs on that eye for awhile before we turn you loose."

"Say, doctor," said Charley, "I want to thank you for taking care of me like you did. I hated to get you out of bed."

"Charley, I'll get out of bed for you anytime, anytime at all. I wish the hell you'd have called me as soon as it happened, though."

"Look, doctor, I've been looking out of one eye for a long time now. I can see all I have to see with it. Even if I lose my right eye, I'm going to be all right."

"I believe you are, Charley," said Dr. Moore, smiling across the bed at Miriam, and Charley, darting his glance from one face to the other, saw the answering smile. "Well, I'll be going now. I'll look in later."

Charley turned to Miriam.

"When I get out of here, Miriam, I've got to find Jack, and when I find him I bet I'll find Ross, too."

"I'll help you look, honey. The first thing I'll do when I get home is write to the orphanage and ask if there were three Morris boys there. I know they won't tell me who adopted who, but they can at least tell me if there were three of you together."

"How's Freddie?" said Charley.

"He's doing fine, honey. He wants to know when you'll be coming home."

"Does he know what happened?" asked Charley.

119

"Of course not, Charley. He's only three years old. All he knows is you're not there to play with him anymore. Whenever he hears a noise outside, he runs to the window to see if it's you."

"Well, tell him I'll be there before he can turn around, and we'll play like we used to."

CHAPTER EIGHTEEN

Charley did not dwell for long on the injury to his right eye. Rather, he was grateful for the sight in his left, recalling the year he had spent inside his prison of bandages, when he was allowed only occasional, blurred glimpses of the world during the changing of the dressings. He remembered all too vividly the flames from which he had escaped, seeing them light the sky again and again as he did as he sat on the ground in Kurmitola, and he considered himself fortunate to be alive at all, even with only one good eye, no ears, crippled hands, a rebuilt nose and quilted face.

As the new skin planted on the burned places took hold and grew, and little by little the gauze came off his neck, face and head, the strength returned to Charley's big frame, sending the remembered vitality of his carefree days shooting through him. A new baby came, Andrew Michael, named for Dr. Moore, and the house in Phoenixville grew too small for them. Charley chafed to return to Alabama and begin living his new life.

"When can I go home to Alabama, doctor?" he asked Dr. Moore. It was Spring, of 1947, and Charley, in the clearness of his mind's eye, saw the farmers following their mules in the peanut and cotton fields, turning with their plows the rich earth of home. He saw the trees already green. The sap was rising everywhere, and in him, too. That Spring, his promotion to major had come through.

Dr. Moore leaned back in his swivel chair in his simple office, looking at Charley through friendly blue eyes.

"I guess you're ready to get going, Charley. I don't blame you. I want you to be patient for a little while, though. You might think you're strong as a bull, but the traveling would knock the hell out of you. Do you know how many times you've been operated on?"

"No, sir, I don't. It seems like there's always somebody cutting on me. How many times, doctor?"

"One of the nurses counted them up this morning. I think you hold the world's record, Charley. You've been in surgery sixty-five times."

"That's a lot of operating, doctor."

"It certainly is, Charley. You've been through hell and back. If I had the time I'd write your case for one of the medical journals. The thing is, and I hate to tell you this, that we're not through yet. We've completed all of the major surgery on your face, neck and head. All we have to do now is scrape off all the rough skin. Also, we're still not satisfied with your nose. We might have to work on that some more. There's nothing to it, but it takes time."

"What about my hands, doctor?"

"That's our biggest concern at the moment. It took a long time for the skin we transplanted to take hold. The truth is, several grafts didn't take and we had to do it over. Now we're ready to start operating on your hands to put them in shape so you can use them. That's going to take time, Charley?"

"How long, doctor?"

122

Dr. Moore stared reflectively at Charley.

"A long time," he said.

"How long?" repeated Charley.

"Maybe two years, Charley."

"Two years?" said Charley. "You mean I won't be able to use my hands for two more years?"

"About that, Charley."

"You mean I'm going to wear these boxing gloves for two more years?"

"That's right, son. We've got to be careful with the small bones in your hands, Charley. We'll have to operate two or three times to save your thumbs and the parts of your fingers you have left. After that, we're going to put you through physical therapy to train you to use your hands again."

"Two years?" said Charley, still incredulous. "I'll be an old man when I get out of here."

Dr. Moore smiled at that.

"That's right, Charley. You'll be an old man of maybe 28 or 29. Don't worry, Charley. The world won't go away while you're recovering. It'll still be there waiting for you."

"Just the same, doctor, I want to get started. I don't need hands for that."

"All right, Charley, I'll work on it. If you're strong enough by the end of the year, I'll let you stay in Alabama between operations, but you won't be discharged from the hospital until we've done all we can for you."

"Okay, doctor. Thanks."

In November, Charley went to surgery for another operation on his hands. Two weeks later, early in December, almost four years after his plane crashed in India, Charley received word that he could move to Alabama.

"You'll be able to spend Christmas at home this year," said Dr. Moore.

Charley and Miriam sold their little house, the only home they'd ever owned, and with the children and their 1947 Oldsmobile sedan they headed south over the mountains for Alabama. While Miriam drove out of the little town, whose inhabitants, accustomed now to the sight of crippled and disfigured servicemen, had been able to look at Charley without wincing, Charley experienced a twinge of uneasiness. What would people who had read and heard only of the glory of war do when they saw his manufactured face? Would they faint, as Miriam had done, although Miriam had not even seen his face but the mask covering it? They would get used to it, he thought, just as he had, thinking how the little lines between the patches of skin had seemed to disappear with constant examination in the mirror. The longer he looked at himself, the more the differing colors of skin, taken from arms, legs, hips and stomach, seemed to come together in one color. His service cap covered red flaps of borrowed skin and only his nose, still being shaped, and his right eye were covered. The black patch over his right eye, he told himself, would be the focus of all attention, anyway, detracting from the other mutilations.

"We'll drive until we get to South Carolina, honey," said Miriam, breaking into his thoughts. "We should get there about nine tonight. We'll stop there for the night and we'll leave early in the morning. We'll be home by tomorrow night."

"That's fine, Miriam," said Charley. "Just take it easy driving. I want to get home in one piece."

Miriam shot a quick glance at him, and, then, realizing what he'd said, Charley began to laugh. Relieved, Miriam began laughing with him. She admired his spirit.

"You're going to be all right, honey," she said, reaching out with her right hand and patting his knee. "Everything's going to be fine."

Relaxed now, all the tension having fled with the laugh on himself, Charley put the big, white ball of his left hand on hers.

"You're right, Miriam," he said, chuckling. "What was it Roosevelt said? The only thing we have to fear is fear itself."

Alert at the start of the long drive to the beauty of the rolling countryside, scenery he had not seen in five years, since he had gone to a place called Kurmitola in India, Charley stared with school-boy awe at the wondrous sights of America. Gradually, though, the strain of the ride and the warmth of the sun wore him down and Charley dozed off.

"Hey, Charley. How you doing, boy?"

"Hey, Jack. Where you been? I've been looking all over for you."

"Didn't I tell you I was going to look for Ross? The last thing Momma said was for me to look after you and Ross. Well, I found you and now I've got to find Ross."

"Where's Momma, Jack? Why did she put us in that place?"

"I've been looking for her, too, Jack. I haven't found her yet. The only reason she sent us away, I figure, was she couldn't take care of us."

"What do you do with yourself, Jack? I mean what kind of work do you do? Every time I see you, you're out looking for somebody."

"I've got to find you people, don't I? Soon as I find Ross and Momma I'm going to look for Daddy. I don't care if I find him or not, though, not after him leaving Momma and us kids the way he did, but I've got to look just the same.

"Why do you want to find him at all, Jack?"

"I want to know where we came from, Charley."

"Say, Jack, are you positively sure that we've got a brother named Ross?"

"What are you going to do when you get out of that hospital for good, Charley? Do you know yet?"

"I don't know, Jack. I used to like fooling around with cars and stuff, but I won't be able to do that with these hands. Maybe I could open a garage and tell people what to do. What do you think, Jack?"

"Well, Charley, all I know is that people who work with their hands only work for wages. They always work for somebody else. So maybe you're lucky you won't be able to work with your hands. Maybe you'll work with your brains. Those are the people who make it, Charley, the people who work with their brains."

"Where did you learn all that, Jack?"

"Traveling around the way I do, looking for people, you're bound to pick up something. Well, so long, Charley. I'll be seeing you."

"Why don't you stick around for a few minutes? Why are you always in such a hurry? Tell me some more about Momma and Ross."

"Next time, Charley. I've got to go now."

Jack walked into the fog and disappeared. Charley raised his head and saw the headlights cutting a yellowish path through the black highway.

"You had a nice little nap, honey," said Miriam. "You've been sleeping for three hours."

"Where are we?" he asked.

"Just outside Raleigh. Want to stop and get something

to eat? We'll be able to find a restaurant in Raleigh."

"What time is it?"

"It's a little before 7. Want to stop here? You tired of riding?"

"No, Miriam. We can make South Carolina before too long. Are the kids all right?"

"They're doing just fine. Let me stop at the next restaurant and I'll get something for us to eat. I think we should wake Freddie and make him eat something."

Later, after they had eaten sandwiches in the car, with a wide-awake Freddie now nestled in his arms, and the baby sleeping on the rear seat in his little crib, while the car rolled through the tunnel of light it built, Charley told Miriam about his brother.

"I wonder why he keeps coming back to see me," he said. "Is it because I've been hurt and he's trying to help me?"

"Sugar," said Miriam, laughing, "it's not your brother coming to see you at all. It's you going to see your brother. Don't you see what's happening? You've been looking for him ever since you were separated at the orphanage."

"He keeps saying he's looking for Ross and Momma. He even said he was going to look for Daddy. I never even heard I had a brother named Ross until he told me about it."

"Listen, Honey," said Miriam, smiling patiently. "You knew about Ross but you just plain forgot. That's all. You were only five when you went to the orphanage. Ross probably was only a baby. Wrapped up like you were all this time you had lots of time to think. Somehow, something clicked in your mind and you remembered Ross."

"But I didn't remember him," said Charley, earnestly. "It was Jack who told me about Ross."

"Whose dream was it, Charles? It was your dream, not Jack's. You said yourself you remembered about Ross after Jack told you about him in the dream. And it's you who's looking for the rest of your family. Wherever Jack is, he's probably doing the same thing. Maybe he even dreams about you the way you dream about him."

"Me and Jack, we used to have a lot of fun," said Charley, smiling. "Somebody whipped me once, maybe my mother, I'm not sure, when I bounced a rock off his head. I guess you're right about who's doing the looking, Miriam. But why should I care about finding my father? I never knew him. I have a vague memory of my mother and I'd like to see her again. Jack said he wanted to find Momma and Daddy so that he would know where he came from. Are you saying that Jack's words are really my thoughts?"

"That's right, honey. You want to know about your parents so that you'll know where you came from, and where they came from. Everybody wants to know about his family."

"Did you write the orphanage, honey?"

"Yes, I did. They never answered. We ought to pay them a visit when we get to Alabama."

It was dusk of the following day when they reached Headland, and Daddy Woods and Aunt Annie pretended that Charley was the same man who had gone to India four years earlier.

"You look fine," said P.A. Woods. "Doesn't he, Annie?"

"Yes, he does, but he could use a little weight, though," said Aunt Annie. "We'll take care of that with some good country ham, corn bread and grits.".

"Freddie looks just like you when you were a little

128

boy," said Daddy Woods. "He's going to grow into a fine man like his father."

"What are your plans, Charley?" said Aunt Annie.

"Well, we figure on building a house just outside Headland, on the road to Dothan. We'll get us a little place to stay until that's ready."

"A little place, my foot," said Daddy Woods. "You'll just stay with us. This is your home, boy. Stay as long as you have to. We've missed you son."

"I've missed you all, too," he said, turning suddenly to look at a faded picture on the wall, to hide the tears blurring his only eye. "It's good to be home again."

CHAPTER NINETEEN

Charley's return was heralded in the local newspapers, which recounted in detail his flying exploits and his fight for survival---"miraculous recovery," one newspaper said---and the friends of his youth who crowded into the Woods house were too overcome to hide their surprise.

"Good Lord, Charley," said Sam Harrell, "what happened to you?"

"When they going to start working on you, Charley?" said Bill Weatherly. "I understand they do amazing things these days with plastic surgery."

"They've been working on me for three years already," said Charley.

"Say, Charley," said Harold Gettins, "I know a fellow who got all shot up in the war and the government gave him a nice pension and he's got a place out in the country where he raises turkeys and chickens. Why don't you get a place like that and raise turkeys and chickens, Charley?"

He walked the streets of Headland and Dothan basking in the light touch of the winter sun, warmer by far than the December sun of Pennsylvania. He was always accompanied by Miriam, and sometimes by Freddie, and Miriam's presence was to identify the tall, strange, scarred man walking beside

130

her. If passersby knew Miriam, they knew him.

"Hey, Charley," they'd say, grabbing his arm, pretending they recognized him. "How you doing, boy? Glad to have you back."

Miriam drove Charley to the orphanage on the edge of Birmingham. They entered the building he remembered so well, and he imagined that if he went upstairs to the dormitory he'd find Jack there.

"May I see Miss Wilson?" he told the girl at the desk.

"Miss Wilson?" she said, lines of puzzlement forming on her forehead. "I don't believe I know a Miss Wilson."

"She used to be here when I was a boy," he said.

"Oh," she said. "Well, she's not here now. Can I help you?"

"I was here about twenty-five years ago with my two brothers. I'm trying to find out what happened to them."

"There was a fire in the office about fifteen years ago, before I came," she said. "All the records up to that time were destroyed. Besides, if they were adopted I couldn't give you that information, anyway."

"Well, maybe somebody here knows what happened to Miss Wilson," he said. "She might be able to tell me something about my brothers."

"Let me call one of the older employes. You can talk to her."

She called to a boy walking down the stairs.

"William, will you go over to the kitchen and ask Mrs. Stenson to come here?"

An old woman arrived several minutes later. She wore a white kitchen gown.

"Mrs. Stenson, this is . . . . I'm sorry, sir, I didn't get your name."

"Charles Woods, ma'am."

"Mr. Woods would like to talk to you, Mrs. Stenson."

"Were you in the war, young feller?" said Mrs. Stenson.

"Yes, ma'am, I was. I was here a long time ago with my two brothers, Mrs. Stenson. I'm trying to find them. I understand the records were burned in a fire."

"You said your name was Woods?"

"That's right, but it was Morris before I was adopted. Charles Morris. My brothers are named Jack and Ross."

"Morris?" she said, putting her hand to her chin. "Morris? You from Birmingham, young feller?"

"I think so, ma'am. I think we came from Birmingham."

"You said your brother was named Jack Morris, one of them?"

"Yes. That's right. You know somebody named Jack Morris?"

"There's a man named Jack Morris in Birmingham. He's an older man, though. He couldn't be your brother. Could he be your father?"

"I'll look him up, ma'am. Maybe he is. Where will I find him?"

"I don't rightly know, young feller, but anybody in Birmingham can tell you. He's in some kind of business."

"What do you think, Miriam?" Charley asked his wife.

"What else can we do, Charles?" she said. "It's all we've got to go on, anyway?

There were three John Morrises and two Jack Morrises in the telephone directory.

"Let's try the Jacks first," said Miriam.

She dialed the first number and placed the receiver against Charley's ear. A woman answered.

"Mr. Jack Morris, please?" he said.

"He's not home yet. Do you want to leave a message? He can call you back in a few minutes."

"I'm not sure I have the right Jack Morris, ma'am. The one I'm looking for should be about 50 years old."

"Wrong Jack Morris," said the lady at the other end, laughing. "The one I've got is only 30."

The second number was a business phone. Jack Morris was in New Orleans.

"Maybe I can help," said the man who had answered. "I'm his partner."

"I don't know if you can or not," said Charley. "The Jack Morris I want is my father. I just got to town. My name is Charley and I've got a brother named Jack."

"Say," said the partner, his voice rising with excitement, "you must be one of the boys he had when he was married the first time."

"I might be, sir. There might have been three of us boys, Jack, Ross and me, Charles."

"That's right. That's right. Jack had three kids, all boys. This is great. He's been looking for you kids for years. Say, he'll be back in a few days. Why don't you tell me how he can reach you? In fact, I'll call him right now and tell him."

"All right, sir. Tell him I'm staying with P.A. Woods in Headland. By the way, do you know anything about my mother?"

There was a long pause.

"Hello, hello," said Charley. "Are you still there?"

"Your mother's dead, son. She died long before the war. I'm sorry to have to tell you this. She got married after she and your Pa broke up, though. She's got a daughter about 19 now, I guess. I know her father. You want to see her?"

"I didn't know I had a sister," said Charley. "Does she live in Birmingham?"

"Yes, she does. She and her father live close to my house. Her name is Elvira Meadows. Let me look up her address. Hold it just a minute."

"I've got a sister," Charley told Miriam. "He's looking up her address."

"Hello," said Jack Morris' partner. "I've got that address for you. It's 150 Mendenhall Drive. Got it?"

"Yes, sir, thanks."

"Good, son. Good. Look, I'm going to call your father as soon as I hang up."

A policeman was standing on the corner. Miriam and Charley walked over and asked directions to Mendenhall Drive. Charley looked away when he saw the pity in the officer's eyes. The policeman looked away, too.

"It's a little way from here, ma'am," he told Miriam. "Go to the end of this street and you'll run into Elm Street. Take your right and go up about a mile. Mendenhall Drive is a big, wide street. You said 150? Okay, take your left. It's about ten blocks down."

Miriam pulled up in front of 150 Mendenhall Drive. It was a two-story white wooden structure.

"You stay here, honey," said Charley. "Let me do this by myself."

He rang the doorbell. A pretty girl with reddish hair opened the inside door and looked through the screen of the outside door. She saw Charley and drew back, putting her hand to her mouth.

"Wh-what do you want?" she stammered.

"I'm your brother," he said, almost stammering, too.

"I don't have any brothers." She started to close the door.

"Wait," said Charley. "Wait. Your mother was my mother, too. She had three sons."

"I don't have any brothers," she repeated, staring with astonished eyes at Charley's face.

"The names are Jack, Ross and Charles. I'm Charles. I'm looking for Jack and Ross."

"I don't have any brothers," she said again, and this time she pushed the door firmly shut.

Charley walked down the steps and waited for Miriam to open the car door for him.

"What happened, hon?" she said.

"She wouldn't even invite me in," said Charley. "She wouldn't listen. She said she didn't have any brothers."

"Let's go home, Charley."

"Yes, Miriam. Let's go home. Maybe my father will get in touch with me. He might know something."

CHAPTER TWENTY

Christmas came, and it came too early for Charley, Miriam, Freddie and baby Andy to spend in the new home they were building, but it was the first Christmas in Alabama in five years for Charley. The floor at the foot of the tall tree in the Woods house was spread with artificial snow, more glittery by far than the real snow of Pennsylvania. On top of the snow were layered the toys and presents for a squealingly happy Freddie. Charley, Miriam, Daddy Woods and Aunt Annie gloried in his delight. The presents which the grown-ups would exchange were piled in a corner behind the tree. This was Freddie's Christmas, and Freddie's tree. Little Andy was too young to care.

At dinner on Christmas Eve, at a table crowded with turkey, ham, yams, cranberry sauce, black-eyed peas and corn bread, Daddy Woods gave the blessing.

"I wish Grandma could have seen how you turned out, Charley," said Daddy Woods. Grandma had died several years earlier. "She'd be right proud of you, son."

"I used to give her a lot of trouble," said Charley, laughing at the memories that flooded his head.

"She only made believe she was angry, Charles," said Aunt Annie.

Later, Freddie lay on the carpeted floor and gaped at all the goodies, waiting for Santa Claus, bag and all, to make his appearance down the tiny chimney leading to the fireplace, not even wondering how such a fat old gentleman could negotiate an opening no larger than his leg. Charley and Miriam, sitting on the sofa beside the fire, smiled at each other as Freddie nodded and valiantly lost his battle to stay awake.

The telephone rang. Daddy woods answered it.

"For you, Charley," he said,

He held the receiver for Charley.

"Hello," said Charley.

"This is Jack Morris," said the caller. "You Charles Woods? Used to be Charles Morris?"

"Yes," said Charley. "Are you my father?"

"Yes, son. I've been hunting for you, for you, Jack and Ross, too. Nobody would tell me what happened to you. When can we get together?"

"I'll have to go back to the hospital in a few days. If you come down before New Year's I'll still be here."

"I'll try to make it, son. I've got to run over to New Orleans this week, though. I'll let you know. Do you know where Jack and Ross are?"

"No, I don't. I was hoping you'd know. I heard my mother died."

"That's right, boy. She passed away in 1937. She had a daughter, though. Did you get to see her?"

"Yes. She doesn't know anything about Jack and Ross, either."

"Well, son, I've got to hang up now. We'll get together real soon. Merry Christmas, son."

"Merry Christmas," said Charley. "Good-by."

Daddy Woods hung up the phone, with a pretended nonchalance.

"That was my real father, Dad," he said.

"I know," said Daddy Woods.

"He was just a voice on the telephone, Dad," he said. "You're the only father I ever knew."

Daddy Woods coughed and put his hand on Charley's shoulder.

"This is the nicest Christmas of my life, Charley," he said.

CHAPTER TWENTY ONE

It was the day after New Year's. The house was quiet now, after all of the holiday festivites. The noises of the football games blaring out of the radios strategically placed throughout the house, so that Daddy Woods would miss none of the important plays, in any of the games, had faded away. Aunt Annie and Miriam said they could still hear the yelling, though. Miriam packed Charley's bag for the trip back to Valley Forge, where he was to undergo the first of a series of corrective operations on his hands. Charley sat in the living room, watching Freddie play with one of the toys, a tractor, which he had not yet destroyed. Daddy Woods held a newspaper in front of his face, as though he were reading it.

"When will you be back, Charley?" he said, lowering the paper.

"In a couple of weeks, Dad," he said. "They'll operate as soon as I get there. I'll have to stay in the hospital for about ten days after that."

"The foundation should be up on the new house by that time," said Daddy Woods. "They'll be able to finish it in no time when that's done."

"I figure we'll be able to move in about March," said Charley. "I'd like for Miriam and the boys to stay here while

I'm gone, but she wants to visit her folks for awhile. I hope you don't mind, Dad."

"This is their home, just like it's yours," said Daddy Woods. "They're always welcome whenever they want to come."

Daddy Woods lifted the paper again. He coughed and lowered it.

"Say, Charley, did your father ever get in touch with you again?"

"Who?" said Charley.

"Your father. Jack Morris. Didn't he call back?"

Charley laughed.

"I almost forgot about him, Dad. No. He didn't call. You know, I wouldn't know what to say to him. I never saw him. I don't even know what he looks like."

"He's your father, son."

"You're my father," said Charley.

Miriam entered with Charley's suitcase.

"Time to go, hon," she said. "It's a long way to the airport."

It wasn't until he was on the plane that he realized how much he had come to depend on Miriam. He looked at the food in the tray placed in front of him, unable to hold a fork or a spoon in his hand. A stewardess saw him staring helplessly at the food.

"I guess I'd better help you with that, major," she said.

"Would you?" he said, gratefully.

Later, after she'd fed him, Charley listed her with the angels who had flown with him during his long race with death. She came to his seat just before the plane landed in Philadelphia.

"You'll need some help with your bag," she said. "I'll

140

meet you at the baggage counter after we land."

She carried his bag to the taxi stand outside the terminal. He realized the importance of hands at Suburban Station, when he left the cab and started to pay his fare. He looked at the cabbie in dismay, holding out his bandaged hands.

"That's all right," said the cabbie. "I'll get your wallet for you. Where is it?"

Charley put the club of his left hand on his left hippocket. The cabbie removed the wallet, held it in front of Charley and opened it.

"It's $1.80, major."

"Take a five and give me two dollars back," said Charley.

"No, thanks. I won't let you tip me. I should tip you."

He took $1.80 out of the $5 bill, placed twenty cents in Charley's coat pocket and three dollars back in the wallet. He put the wallet in Charley's hippocket. He placed the bag on the train.

"Good night," he said, and he saluted him. Charley put his right hand to his head in an awkward return.

At the hospital, the cabbie who drove Charley from the train carried Charley's bag to the front desk. He fished the wallet out of Charley's pocket and counted out his fare. He took the tip offered him. There were too many disabled people in Phoenixville for a cabbie to refuse a tip. Most of their business came from the hospital.

Charley checked in and was shown to his old room.

He was awakened by Jean Gazinski.

"Hey, major, glad to have you back. Ready to eat?"

Charley opened his eye and looked at the smiling face of the orderly.

"Hi, Jean. You still here?"

"Yep. I like it here. I think I'll be here when they close down the joint."

"Anything happen around here while I was away?"

"Are you kidding? What's going to happen around here?"

"What happened to Tom Atkinson? Is he still here?"

"They sent him home. They fitted him out with a pair of arms and he learned to use them real quick."

"Say, Jean, let me get cleaned up a little before you feed me, will you?"

"Sure. Take your time. I can't do anything until I feed you, anyway."

Charley returned from the bathroom and sat in a chair beside the bed. Jean fed him, chattering all the while.

"When you get ready to come with me to South Philly for a real meal, let me know. I'll treat you to a feed like you never had before in your life."

"One of these days I'll take you up on that, and you'll be broke for the rest of the month."

"That's a deal," said Jean, laughing.

Dr. Moore entered as Charley finished breakfast.

"Hi, doc, how you doing," said Jean.

"Fine, Jean. Fine. Good morning, Charley. Ready for some work?"

"Good morning, doctor. I'm ready when you are."

"That's good, Charley. We'll let you rest for a couple of days first. We're going to work on both hands at the same time, Charley. While you're down there we'll do some more work on your nose. We should finish with your nose this trip. It looks like all it needs is a little shaping job."

"When you've got me under, I wish you'd do all you have to do at one time. I'm anxious to get home. I've got a house going up and I want to get back before they finish it."

"I'm proud of you, Charley. You've kept yourself in real good shape, and I'm happy about your attitude. A lot of boys just turn their faces to the wall and try to die. You toughed it out, though, and you came through a helluva bad fight. You're the talk of the hospital, Charley. We're all proud of you."

"Come on, doctor. Quit feeding me all that Irish bull."

Charley, putting on a gruff front, pretended he was not moved by Dr. Moore's little speech.

Two mornings later, he was wheeled down to surgery. All he remembered until he woke up in the recovery room was counting backwards from 10. He thought he reached 6 this time. His hands were numb and there was a prickly sensation around his nose. He'd been in surgery enough times to know that the work on his nose had been minor. There would be no pain there, but when the numbness in his hands wore off, he knew, it would be replaced by pain so intense that it would take all the strength of his mind to fight off a demand for drugs.

The pain came, in due time, and he tried to drown it out of his mind with a flood of thoughts of home. He saw the faces of Miriam and Freddie, and the face of Jack.

"How you doing, Charley?"

"Jack. What are you doing here? I thought you were never coming back to see me."

"I thought I'd just drop in and say hello."

"Did you find Ross, Jack?"

"No, Charley. I'm still looking, though."

"Say, Jack. I found out about Momma. She's dead, Jack. She died in Birmingham a long time ago."

"I don't believe it, Charley. I would have known about

it if Momma died. Who told you something like that, anyway."

"It's the truth, Jack. Honest. I went to her house. She had a daughter. Her name is Elvira. I asked her about you and Ross. She didn't know anything about you. She didn't know anything about me, either."

"I suppose you found Dad, too."

"Yes, I did, Jack. I was going to tell you about that. He lives in Birmingham. I talked to him on the phone."

"Look, Charley, I don't care what you say. I don't believe Momma's dead. I would have known, I tell you. Where did you say she used to live?"

"It's 150 Mendenhall Drive, Jack. You want me to tell you how to get there?"

"When I get to Birmingham, all I have to do is ask somebody. I'd better get started."

"Good-by, Jack. Good luck to you."

"Good luck to you, Charley."

When he telephoned Miriam that night, from the bedside phone, with a nurse dialing for him and holding the receiver to his ear, Charley told her he had seen Jack again.

"I think you're right, Miriam. It wasn't Jack looking for me. It was me looking for him. I remember when we were kids. He was always taking care of me. Momma wasn't there, and I didn't know anything about a father. When I was real sick, I just went back in my dreams to somebody who used to look out for me when I was little. Jack was the only one. Poor Jack. He had nobody to dream about when he's in trouble. There was nobody watching out for him."

"One of these days, you'll find your brothers, honey, and it won't be in your dreams. When you coming home?"

"In about ten days. By the way, Dr. Moore says I'm doing fine."

CHAPTER TWENTY TWO

Dr. Moore pronounced Charley ready to travel again, and Charley made reservations for the flight to Dothan, the airport city nearest his home. It was January 22, 1948, another date he would never forget. The flight was scheduled to depart at 1 o'clock in the afternoon.

"Leaving again, huh?" said Jean Gazinski as she fed Charley his breakfast.

"That's right, Jean. This time I won't have to be back for ninety days."

"How you getting to the airport?"

"I figure I'll take a cab to the railroad station and get a cab there for the airport."

"Look, this place is surrounded by Red Cross girls and a bunch of shiny station wagons. They're here for people like you. Why don't you ask one of them to drive you to the airport? This way, you can make 25 miles in less than an hour. You go fooling with cabs and trains and changing from one to the other, it'll take you three or four hours."

"Are you sure they'll give me a ride?"

"That's what they're here for. Those station wagons are parked out there all day, and all they've been doing that I can see is taking guys to football and basketball games. I don't see why they can't haul you over to the airport. It won't kill them."

"Well, I guess I can talk to them about it, anyway. Right, Jean?"

"Right. It won't hurt to talk to them. Look at me. I've been talking to them for four years and I'm not dead yet."

With Jean's help, he donned his uniform. He still had difficulty fitting the bundles of his hands into the slit sleeves of his jacket, but that task performed he walked downstairs to see the Red Cross.

It was one of those Pennsylvania winter days when a mere wisp of a cloud can veil the sun and rob the earth of all its warmth, and when Charley walked down the steps to talk to a girl behind the wheel of a station wagon a fresh blast of wind, contrasting sharply with the toasty warmth of the hospital, whipped through his clothing. His trousers seemed to stiffen with the cold and his legs burned as they rugged against his pants. The freezing air penetrated the bandages of his hands and set them to tingling. His new nose, uncovered for the first time, felt like a cube of ice against his face. Although morning, the day was as dark as dusk.

He put his face against the window of one of the station wagons lined up at the curb. The girl lowered the window. The motor was running, and he put his head inside to catch some of the hot air coming out of the heater.

"Yes, major?" said the girl. "What can I do for you?"

"I've got to go to the airport. I was hoping you could give me a ride."

"Oh, I'm sorry," she said, with a little smile of apology, "but we're not supposed to drive anybody who can walk. It's the rule."

She started to put up the window. Charley, fearing

146

decapitation, removed his head immediately. He walked back up the steps and met another Red Cross girl striding briskly and jauntily out of the building.

"Miss," he said, stopping her in stride, "is there any way I can get a ride to the airport?"

"Certainly," she said, smiling at him as the other had done. "There's a phone booth in the corridor. You'll be able to call a taxi there."

He stood on the steps, in spite of the bitter cold, and watched other patients stream down the steps and enter the vehicles.

"Where are they going?" he asked one of the nurses who had accompanied the patients to the station wagons.

"Oh, did you want to go?" she said. "They're going to Gettysburg for some sight-seeing."

"No," he said. "I was trying to get a ride to the airport."

"They don't do that," she said. "They just take the boys on trips and things. If you weren't able to walk, though, I'm sure arrangements could be made."

Charley climbed up the steps to his floor. Jean Gazinski was joking with two patients at the end of the hall. She saw Charley and walked over to him.

"Hey, major, what happened?"

They couldn't give me a ride. They said they couldn't drive anybody who could walk."

"What about all those guys I just saw jumping in those station wagons? I didn't see any wheelchairs under them. I bet some of those guys could play for Notre Dame right now."

"You can't blame the girls, Jean. That was a planned trip or something. As for the guys, I wouldn't want to deprive them of a chance to have a little fun."

"Hey, I just thought of something," said Jean, snapping her fingers. "I can get somebody to swap shifts with me. I'll drive you to the airport in my jalopy. It ain't much, but it'll get us there."

"No, Jean, but thanks. I've got to start getting used to the way things are. There's one thing you can do for me, though. You can call a cab."

At the railroad station, Charley stared helplessly at the taxi driver.

"Want me to get your wallet, major?" he said.

Charley nodded and patted his left hip pocket with his club of a hand.

"Add a fifty cents tip," he said.

It was an hour's ride to Philadelphia on the local line. The conductor placed Charley's bag on the platform. Charley stood by it, hoping that one of the rushing throng would grasp his predicatement and stop. It was a long walk from the track level to the upstairs exit. He knew it was a long walk by the long line of people headed in the one direction and ascending a distant stairway. Finally, a straggler, a youth of 18 or 19 sauntered by, not hurrying as the others.

"Say, kid," called Charley.

The youth stopped and stared at Charley's patched-up face.

"Can I help you, major?" he said.

"I wish you would," said Charley. "I can't use my hands and I've got to get this bag up to a taxi stand. I'll give you a dollar to carry it for me."

"I don't need a dollar to do that, major," said the boy, taking up the bag. "Let's go."

The cab pushed through the busy Philadelphia traffic,

stopping and starting at the lights on the long stretch of Broad Street. When he arrived at the airport, Charley looked at his watch. It was 12:15, 45 minutes to departure time. It had taken him three hours and thirty minutes to travel the 25 miles from Valley Forge General Hospital.

Again, the cabbie took his fare and tip from Charley's wallet, and the same procedure was repeated with the porter who carried his bag upstairs to the ticket counter.

Miriam met him at the airport, and Charley, still smoldering at his inability to do things for himself, was an irate man. Miriam felt the tenseness when they embraced.

"What's the matter, Charles?" she said. "What's wrong? You're wound up like a rattlesnake getting ready to strike."

"You know what I'm waiting for, Miriam?" he replied. "I'm waiting for the day when I carry my own luggage and count my own money."

"Why don't you let me go back with you, hon?" said Miriam. "I can take care of all those little things until you're able to do them yourself."

"No, honey. I want you to stay here and take care of the kids. Besides, we've got a house to build. Somebody has to watch over things when I'm not around."

CHAPTER TWENTY THREE

Gentled by Miriam's presence, and never one to keep hold of his anger, anyway, Charley turned his mind to important things, like Miriam, the children and the new house.

For the next three months, Charley spent his days watching his house go up, recommending changes, getting in the way of the builders, planning the landscaping. His nights were spent with Miriam and the children. Freddie still liked to wrestle on the floor with his father.

The house was ready for occupancy in April, and Charley carried all of them, Miriam, Freddie and Andy, over the threshold.

"Well," he said, putting them down, "we're home."

"That's right," said Miriam. "Home at last."

Charley was due to return to Valley Forge in a week. That week was spent in entertaining the people of Dothan and Headland who came by the dozens to see the house that Charley built. It was a rambling, ranch-style building that was constructed big enough to accommodate the dozen children Miriam said she was going to have. It took all of Charley's savings.

Daddy Woods and Aunt Annie came to call, ringing the

front doorbell of the brand new Woods home.

"What are you doing ringing the bell?" said Charley, sternly. "This is your house, too. The door is always open. Just come on in anytime."

He dreaded the trips to Valley Forge, the long waits at railroad stations, airports and taxi stands, still not hardened by the pitying stares he encountered wherever he went. At the hospital, he was not a curiosity. He hated the waiting for somebody to offer to carry his bag, always holding the boxing gloves on his hand in front of him, in plain view, so people would understand why he waited with such patient suffering. It embarrassed him yet to have to ask a cab driver or a store clerk to reach into his pocket and count out the money Charley owed.

Still, he grew stronger, and he felt that he could tear down walls with his hard body. He felt secure and safe only in Alabama and in the hospital, though, where he recognized the faces he saw, faces that did not register shock, pity or astonishment at the sight of him.

On his second trip back to Valley Forge, in March of 1949, he received a visit late one night from Dr. Moore.

"I wanted to see you before I leave, Charley," he said. "I just got my discharge."

"Gosh, doctor, you can't leave me. I want you to stick around until I'm well enough to be discharged, too."

"You're all right, Charley. A couple of more operations and you'll be out of here, too. My work is done, Charley. I've got to get back to private practice and start helping civilians."

They shook hands and Dr. Moore turned to leave.

"Wait, doctor," said Charley, and he remembered how he had called after Jack in the same way in his dreams. He smiled at the recollection.

"What is it, Charley?" said Dr. Moore, taking his hand from the doorknob and turning to face him.

"Nothing," he replied, lamely. "I just wanted to wish you the best of everything."

He didn't want to tell the doctor that, at that instant, when he was walking out of his life, he felt again that he was being abandoned.

On that visit, the boxing gloves were removed from Charley's hands. Charley saw that he had lost all of his digits except his thumbs and two stubs of fingers on each hand. Physical therapists worked on his hands to revive them from their four-year-long state of immobility. He learned to use his thumbs, although they felt to him like extra appendages which had been fastened to his hands and might fall off at any moment. Gradually, the bones in his hand took on new life.

This time when he was sent home to recuperate, he felt less like a cripple than he had since the full impact of what had happened to him hit him in the hospital in Calcutta. He was able to carry his own bag by slipping the handle over his hand and letting it slide down to the crook of his elbow. He could take his wallet out of his pocket, but he wasn't able yet to count his money for fares and tips. His amputated fingers were still covered for protection against contact.

"One more trip and we'll be through with you," said the doctor who had taken Dr. Moore's place, Captain James Jensen. "Come back in three months or so and we'll take a look at you and send you on your way."

Back home, he told Miriam he was just about ready to be a civilian again.

"What do you think you're going to do, honey?" she said.

"Well," he said, putting a serious note in his voice, "I was thinking about what one of those people here told me on the street one day. He said I should raise turkeys and chickens and collect a government pension. What do you think of that?"

Miriam looked at him with eyes widened with surprise.

"Is that what you want to do?" she said, trying to hide the increduilty in her voice. "Is that what you really want?"

Charley laughed and grabbed her, and released her immediately, remembering her delicate condition. She was pregnant again.

"Are you all right, honey?" he said. "Did I hurt you?"

"Of course not, silly," she said. "You didn't answer me. Is that what you really want to do, sit back and raise turkeys and chickens."

"Heck, no, Miriam," he said, laughing at her. "You know me better than that. God didn't give me back my life so that I would waste it away sitting back and collecting a pension. I remember something Jack told me in one of those nightmares I had. He told me that the people who do things are those who work with their brains. I'm going to put my mind to work for me, Miriam. That's what I'm going to do."

"It wasn't Jack who told you that," said Miriam, patiently, as though she had explained this to him many times before. "It was your dream, and the words Jack said came out of your head."

"You know, that's strange," he said, shaking his head in amazement. "I haven't dreamed about Jack in a long time. I wonder why that is."

"You don't need him anymore, that's why, honey."

"Is that why, you reckon?" he said.

When he was discharged from the hospital in March,

153

1950, five years and three months after 28,000 pounds of gasoline exploded under him, with all the dressings gone and his hands functioning again, functioning as well as they could, under the circumstances, Charley walked down the steps with his bag in his hand---in his hand, and not the crook of his elbow. He turned at the bottom and backed to the curbing, gazing with affection at the big, sprawling place that had been so much a part of him since the beginning of 1945. The faces of the doctors, nurses, orderlies, patients---Tom Atkinson, Hugh Longo, Pat Murphy, Scotty Prothro, Big John Rodoff---marched in smiling, disordered review through his mind. Dr. Moore smiled benevolently at him. Jean Gazinski showed him a happy grin. Once again the voice of Dr. Hull came to him from Calcutta, "Make sure they take you to Valley Forge General Hospital."

He stood against the wall and waited for the taxi to take him to the Phoenixville station for the last time. The March sun was warm against the bricks, although the wind still held the chill of winter in it. In the sky, the sun came out from behind a white cloud, and looking at the bright world stretching before him, he murmured, there in the quiet space he occupied, the same prayer he'd said at the start of every flying mission.

"Dear God, please be with us," he said, and the taxi came and took him away.

-- The End --

EPILOGUE

Charley Woods drove a new pickup truck into the driveway of his home. He honked the horn. Miriam came to the door with the baby in her arms. Freddie followed close behind and shot around his mother to jump on the running board.

"Where did you get that, hon?" said Miriam.

"I just bought it," said Charley. "Ain't it a beauty. It's our first investment."

"Investment? What investment? What are you talking about, Charley?"

"We're in the construction business, Miriam. I bought the truck and a lot to build a house on. Now I'm going out to hunt me some people who know how to build houses."

"Do you have any money to do that? I mean, there isn't much left, is there?"

"There's a little left from my military pay, Miriam, not much, though. What I did was, I bought the truck and then I mortgaged it to the bank for the money to buy the lot."

Miriam walked to the side of the truck and smiled at the proud figure of her husband, who was confidently setting out to conquer the world in a khaki shirt, denim pants and a floppy hunting cap.

Charley sat on the truck's high seat as on a throne, beaming back at her, master of all he surveyed, particularly of himself.

"We're in business, Miriam," he said. "We're going to knock them dead. I'm going to hire me some people to do what I tell them and I'm going to spread my houses all over Alabama."

"I know you will, hon. I know you will," she said, and she reached in the window to grasp one of his crippled hands.

Charley built not one house but two on his lot, on a corner in Dothan. He borrowed money on his car to pay the workers until he found buyers, and both houses were sold.

He hired more men and built more houses, and in less than six months Charley Woods was the biggest home builder in Southeast Alabama. The money he earned went back in the business. Charley and Miriam made do with only the necessities of living, putting off until later the acquisiton of a new car, newer furniture and a television set.

Charley's construction company grew and he moved into the field of housing developments, putting them wherever he found the land, taking advantage of the population expansion and the resultant demand for housing space. He and Miriam still resisted the temptation to spend their money on luxuries. Rather, he invested in pecan groves and watermelon farms.

Miriam tried to give Charley the dozen children they wished for, but she stopped at 10 after their last child, Cynthia Mary, died when she was three weeks old. Frederick Charles, the Freddie of their Valley Forge days, died at 19 after a series of illnesses. Charley and Miriam adopted a boy, Ronald Grady, to save him from a brutal stepfather. The oldest of the remaining nine children is Andrew Michael, 26, and the youngest is Cathy Lou, 10. Between them are Richard Pleasant, Jonathan Wilkes, Deborah Ann, Ruth Ellen, Ronald Grady, David Dwight and Timothy Lee.

Charley never knew when he became a millionaire, and he probably wouldn't have known it then except his accountant told him. It was the same accountant who had been retained to examine Charley's books after his first year in business.

"Charles," he said, "tell me this. How much money did you put into this building business to get it started?"

"Nothing," said Charley.

"Nothing?" said the accountant.

"That's right," said Charley. "Nothing."

"That explains it, then," said the accountant. "I've been chasing this rabbit in and out of this hole for two hours looking for your original investment. That explains it. Nothing, huh?"

"Nothing," repeated Charley.

Charley kept building. He invested in farmlands in Alabama and apartment complexes in Florida, oil wells in Texas, advertising firms in Atlanta and Dallas. Before he realized it, Charles Woods, a man who had died several times on the operating table, who was compelled to work with his mind because he could do nothing else, controlled an international empire. His holdings included an electronic research firm in Bermuda, a motion picture production company in New York and Italy and a woodworking plant in West Virginia. At the same time, he owned majority interest in radio and television stations in his home town of Dothan and in Macon, Georgia.

In 1953, his right eye became infected again, the eye which had been injured in the wrestling game with Freddie in

Phoenixville. It was removed in a Birmingham hospital.

He was named to the Alabama Prison Board in 1954, and he tried to reform the prison system. Particularly, he conducted an investigation to determine why prisoners who were able to afford high-priced lawyers could receive pardons and paroles while inmates without money were likely to serve their full terms. He likes to think that his efforts brought about some reforms, but feels there still is much room for improvement.

A millionaire ten times over, and his businesses continuing to grow, Charley Woods entered the field of politics himself. He ran for governor twice, spending his own money, accepting very few contributions. In 1966, he finished fifth in a field of ten, his biggest satisfaction being that he ran ahead of two former governors. In 1970, he ran third behind Governor Albert Brewer and former Governor George Wallace.

One-eyed and with crippled hands, Charley does not look on himself as being handicapped physically. He was visiting his farm in Dothan one day in 1963. He saw a big stallion rampaging around the corral.

"That a new horse?" he asked a hand.

"Yes, sir," was the reply. "He's sort of wild. We can't get anybody to break him yet."

"Let me try him," said Charley.

He stayed on the bucking horse for five seconds, according to the hired hand's count, and when he was thrown he landed on his back. He was in the hospital with a broken back for three weeks and wore a brace for seven months. The pain he suffered during that period reminded him of the agonies he endured during the reconstruction surgery at Valley Forge General Hospital. Two days after his release from the hospital in Dothan, he decided to travel to Panama City, Florida, for a few days on his cabin cruiser. A local friend, Rufus Davis, drove the car. He proceded cautiously because of Charley's injury. A pick-up truck entered the highway from a side road and turned the wrong way on the one-way street. The vehicles met head-on.

"Charley," said the doctor who treated him at the hospital, from which he had just been discharged, "is there any way we can keep you out of here?"

His injuries were not serious, however. The doctor picked glass out of his head for two hours and sent him home. His friend, Rufus Davis, was not hurt.

In 1969, he was named American of the Year by the American Bowl in Tampa, Florida, an annual event featuring All-America football players. The Bowl also honors outstanding citizens.

Daddy Woods and Aunt Annie live near Charley, in Dothan, and his adopted father, still spry and active at 75, works in Charley's main office, a favorite of the people who help run the Woods international spread.

One-tenth of what Charley earns goes to the church, believing it was part of God's plan for him to go through the fire, like steel, so that he would be a better man. When he began tithing, he had little he could give. Now, his accountants compute how much he owes to the works of the Lord. He's not a joiner and belongs to only one organization, the Calvary Baptist Church, of which he is a deacon. Also, he gives generously to many worthy causes, and his heart opens wider when children are involved.

It was several years after they talked on the telephone that he met his real father, Jack Morris, but he never found his brothers. Their trail always ended at the Mercer Orphans

Home. Wherever he goes, he makes it a point to say that his name used to be Charles Morris and he has two missing brothers, Jack and Ross. He's hoping that somebody, someday, will remember.

But Charley no longer bothers about his roots. He has stopped searching for his own identity. He found it, although it was years before he understood, in the flaming crash of a plane in Kurmitola, India.